ACCESS TO 200+ SARASOTA RESTAURANT MENUS

The
Little Sarasota
DINING
Book.

dS
dineSARASOTA

2024

OUR 15TH ANNUAL EDITION!!

SARASOTA'S BEST SELLING RESTAURANT GUIDE

DINESARASOTA.COM

The Little Sarasota DINING Book.
15th Edition | 2024

To contact us, please send email to:
press@dinesarasota.com

Printed in the USA

10 9 8 7 6 5 4 3 2 1

ISBN 978-0-9862840-9-0

THANK YOU!

Thanks for picking up the 15th edition of our annual Sarasota dining book. We are so happy to be able to give you Sarasota restaurant information that you can use every day! But like most things in life, we couldn't do it without help.

Thanks to Nicole Bonsall, Stephanie Brown, Terry Daniels, Sandra Frank, Debbie Hoffman, Lauren Jackson, Sharon Kunkel, Ken Shiro Lumpkin, Brynn Murray, Lorenzo Muslia, Claudia Potes, Jacque Slayton, Dimitri Syros, Bruno Toso, and Kaye Warr for contributing content to this year's edition. It is fantastic to have such talented people in our community. And we're grateful for their help.

Cindi Kievit (print & digital), Jen Hogan (digital), and Anna Denton (digital) make sure it's actually possible for you to read all things we write about. Thank you for your editing skills and masterful use of the red pen.

As always, thanks to you! Thank you for supporting what we do. We're always striving to make sure that our local Sarasota restaurants get the attention they so richly deserve. I know that they appreciate you too!

It's our 15th edition! That is hard to imagine. Time flies when you're having fun. That much is for sure. ☺

There have been some changes to our local Sarasota dining community all that time. Happily, lots of fantastic restaurants have opened. And sadly, some have closed. Things change. And that's OK. The culinary world moves fast. It would be horrible for Sarasota to be left too far behind.

We've added lots more depth to our choices. Yes, there are lots more taco places. But now we actually have a selection of Indian restaurants (and delis)! There's Thai and sushi on nearly every corner, but also a dim sum spot (or two).

As our numbers here in Sarasota have grown over those 15 years, so has our diversity of cuisine. Don't get me wrong; you know I love a good burger. But a steamy, satisfying bowl of ramen also has a place in my heart.

There's been an unending influx of "upscale" chains. But also a big surge in independently owned restaurants. It's these "indies" that keep our choices refreshing. They're sometimes small enough to fill a niche that the big boys either can't figure out or just don't care enough about.

It's hard to imagine what the next 15 will bring to our once small but mighty dining scene. One thing is for certain. Change will come. Some of it will be for the better, some not so much. But we'll eat our way through all of it.

Thanks for all the support for our work over the past 14 editions. We appreciate you!

Larry Hoffman
Publisher, dineSarasota.com

dS
dineSARASOTA

2024 DINESARASOTA TOP 50

- [ ] 1   Shebeen Irish Pub & Kitchen *
- [ ] 2   Osteria Southside *
- [ ] 3   Florence and the Spice Boys *
- [ ] 4   Beso *
- [ ] 5   The Chateau Sarasota *
- [ ] 6   Bar Hana *
- [ ] 7   Palm Avenue Deli *
- [ ] 8   GROVE Restaurant
- [ ] 9   Faicco's Italian Hero's & Grill
- [ ] 10   Michael's on East
- [ ] 11   Bijou Garden Cafe
- [ ] 12   Mattison's Forty One
- [ ] 13   Azul Steak & Sushi Lounge *
- [ ] 14   Drunken Poet Cafe
- [ ] 15   JR's Old Packinghouse Café
- [ ] 16   Bay Leaf Indian Cuisine *
- [ ] 17   Duval's Fresh. Local. Seafood.
- [ ] 18   Tzeva *
- [ ] 19   Meshugana Deli *
- [ ] 20   Pier 22
- [ ] 21   Capo Pazzo *
- [ ] 22   Walt's Fish Market & Restaurant
- [ ] 23   Deep Lagoon Seafood & Oyster *
- [ ] 24   Namo Izakaya *
- [ ] 25   Pho Cali
- [ ] 26   Tripletail Seafood & Spirits
- [ ] 27   The Breakfast Company
- [ ] 28   Meliora
- [ ] 29   The Cottage

☐	30	Island House Tap & Grill
☐	31	Karl Ehmer's Alpine Steak House
☐	32	Fork & Hen
☐	33	Post Kitchen & Bar *
☐	34	Old Salty Dog
☐	35	Brick's Smoked Meats
☐	36	Cafe L'Europe
☐	37	Sage
☐	38	Phillippi Creek Oyster Bar
☐	39	A Sprig of Thyme
☐	40	Harry's Continental Kitchens
☐	41	Crab & Fin
☐	42	Libby's Neighborhood Brasserie
☐	43	1592 Wood Fired Kitchen
☐	44	The Mable
☐	45	Selva Grill
☐	46	Crow's Nest
☐	47	Rosemary and Thyme
☐	48	Pop's Sunset Grill
☐	49	Beach House
☐	50	Amore Restaurant

* Opened since our last edition.

HOW TO USE THIS CHECKLIST - Like you really need an explanation for this. But, just in case, here goes. Get out there and eat through our Top 50! We've made it easy for you to keep track of your culinary adventures. These are the restaurants that you've been searching for, clicking on, and downloading on our dineSarasota.com website all year. So, in a way, this is really *your* Top 50. And, if you flip to the back of this book, we've left a couple of note pages for you to keep track of your favorites. Go ahead, start your own Sarasota restaurant journal.

HOW TO USE THIS BOOK

Thanks for picking up a copy of the latest *Little Sarasota DINING Book*. We're hoping that you're going to use it as your go-to guide to Sarasota dining. Now that you're the proud owner of a copy, we're going to give you some helpful inside tips on how to use the guide.

First off, it's arranged alphabetically. So, if you know the alphabet, you can use our guide. Yes, it's really that easy. It has basic restaurant information in each listing. Name, address, phone… it also lists the restaurant's website if you would like to go there for additional information.

In the outlined bar, it will tell you the neighborhood/area where the restaurant is located, the cuisine it serves, and its relative expense. It's relative to Sarasota, not NYC; keep that in mind.

We list the hours of operation for each restaurant. It helps to know when they are open. We try our best to make this info as accurate as possible. But sometimes, Sarasota restaurants have special seasonal hours. We apologize in advance if a place may have changed their hours after we went to print. If there's a question, it's always best to call the restaurant.

For each place we'll also tell you what you can expect. Is it noisy or quiet? Good for kids? Maybe a late night menu. It's not an exhaustive list, just some of the highlights to guide your dining decision-making process.

We'll give you a few Best Bites. It's a quick look at what's on the menu. Again, we try our best to keep these current, but...

There aren't a lot of mysterious symbols that you have to reference. If you see this *, it means the restaurant has more than one location. We've listed what we consider to be the main one. The other locations are usually listed in the super handy cross reference in the back of the book.

Speaking of the cross reference, here's the scoop. Restaurants are listed in alphabetical order (you're good at that now!). We give you basic info: Name, address, phone. Restaurants are then listed by cuisine type and then by location. So, you can easily find that perfect seafood restaurant on Longboat Key.

QR CODES. Each restaurant listing has a little square box with a bunch of jumbled up dots. That's your easy access to the menu for that restaurant. Just scan that little code with the QR reader or camera on your smartphone and, just like magic, there's the menu! Pretty great, right? Oh, what if I don't have a smartphone? Well, then it just might be time...

SPECIALTY CATEGORIES. OK. Here's where things really get interesting. You now know where things are located and what type of food you can expect. But, let's dive in a little deeper. Let's say you're just visiting beautiful, sunny Sarasota AND you've got kids. What would be a good choice? How about celebrating a special occasion or event? Or, maybe you would just like to eat a meal and enjoy a spectacular water view. Where's the best spot?

That's where our specialty categories come in. Here are some things to keep in mind. First, we've curated these restaurant lists just for you. Second, these places may not be the only ones in town that fit the description. But, we think they're among the best. Hey, why isn't my favorite pizza place on that list? We're not trying to snub anybody here, but there's only so much space.

LIVE MUSIC – Really self-explanatory. But, the music ranges from piano bar to acoustic guitar to rock 'n' roll. So, you may want to see who's playing the night you're going. Also, yes, there are other places in town that have live music.

CATERING – You could probably convince most restaurants to cater your twelve person dinner or throw together some to-go food for you to arrange on your own platters. The places listed here do it for REAL. They cater regularly.

EASY ON YOUR WALLET – A little perspective is in order here. Nothing on this list comes close to the McDonald's Dollar Menu (thankfully). That being said, these are some places you could go and not have to sell some jewelry to pay the tab. Something to keep in mind, "Easy on the wallet" depends a little on how big your billfold is. These restaurants won't break the budget.

NEW – No explanation necessary. These restaurants are "relatively" new. Some have been open longer than others. But, they've opened since our last edition.

SPORTS + FOOD + FUN – The big game is on and you want to see it. Here are some places that do that well. Lots of places have a TV in the bar. These go above and beyond that.

GREAT BURGERS – For the past year, our *A Burger A Week* series has been running in our newsletter, *Sarasota Bites*. We'll give you some of the highlights in this burger listing.

NICE WINE LIST – Hmmm… A 2006 Cabernet or a 2015 Pouilly-Fuissé? That is one tough question. No "wine in a box" here. These restaurants all have a sturdy wine list and are proud of it. Sometimes it can certainly be a little intimidating choosing a wine. These spots usually have someone to hold your hand and walk you through it.

A BEAUTIFUL WATER VIEW – Nothing says Florida like a picture perfect view of the water. And, these places have that. The food runs the gamut from bar food to fine dining.

LATER NIGHT MENU – This is not New York, and it is not Miami or Chicago either. That is the context with which you should navigate this list. Notice we said "LATER" night menu and NOT "late night menu." We're a reasonably early dining town. The places listed here are open past the time when half of Sarasota is safely tucked in bed. They might not all be 1AM, but we do have a few choices if you're still out past 2am!

SARASOTA FINE DINING – It's not great when people look down their noses at our upscale dining scene. We have some damn good chefs here in Sarasota. And, they're showing off their skills every single day. They should be celebrated. This list may not contain Le Bernardin, Alinea, or The French Laundry. But, we have some REAL contenders.

Lastly, there is always the question, "How do these restaurants get into this book?" They are selected based on their yearly popularity on dineSarasota.com. These are the restaurants that YOU are interested in. You've been searching for them on our website all year long. There are no advertisements here. So, you can't "buy your way in." It's all you. This is really YOUR guide. And, I must say, you have great taste!

A SPRIG OF THYME

1962 Hillview Street
941-330-8890
asprigofthymesrq.com

SOUTHSIDE VILLAGE	EUROPEAN	COST: $$

HOURS: Tues-Sat, 5PM to 9PM
CLOSED SUNDAY & MONDAY (SUMMER ONLY)

WHAT TO EXPECT: Upscale, Casual • Good For A Date
European Bistro Feel • Good Wine List

BEST BITES: Escargot Gratine • Merou Au Veloute D'epinards
Confit Canard Pyrenees • Noisette D'agneau

SOME BASICS

SCAN FOR MENU

Reservations:	YES
Spirits:	BEER/WINE
Parking:	STREET
Outdoor Dining:	YES

ALMAZONICA CERVECERIA

4141 South Tamiami Trail
941-260-5964
almazonicacerveceria.com

SOUTH TRAIL	PERUVIAN	COST: $$

HOURS: Tues-Sat, 4PM to 10PM
CLOSED SUNDAY & MONDAY

WHAT TO EXPECT: Upscale • Small Batch Cerveceria (Brewery)
"Amazon Soul" • Lots Of Parking

BEST BITES: Ceviche! • Corazon Mio Anticucho
Arroz con Mariscos • Peruvian Churros • Pan Roasted Cod

SOME BASICS

SCAN FOR MENU

Reservations:	YES
Spirits:	BEER/WINE
Parking:	LOT
Outdoor Dining:	NO

ALPINE STEAKHOUSE & BUTHER SHOP

4520 South Tamiami Trail
941-922-3797
alpinesteak.com

SOUTH TRAIL	AMERICAN	COST: $$

HOURS: Tue to Sat, 9AM to 9PM
CLOSED SUNDAY & MONDAY

WHAT TO EXPECT: Great Butcher Shop • Home Of The "TurDuckHen"
German Cuisine • Featured On The Food Network

BEST BITES: TurDuckHen • Steaks! • 1/2lb Sirloin Burger
German Sausage Sampler • Texas Baby Back Ribs

SCAN FOR MENU

SOME BASICS
Reservations:	NO
Spirits:	FULL BAR
Parking:	LOT
Outdoor Dining:	NO

AMA LA VITA RISTORANTE

1551 Main Street
941-960-1551
amalavitasrq.com

DOWNTOWN	ITALIAN	COST: $$$

HOURS: Wed-Sat, 5PM to 9PM
CLOSED SUNDAY, MONDAY & TUESDAY

WHAT TO EXPECT: Upscale Italian • Private Dining Available
Good Wine List • Downtown Location

BEST BITES: Artichoke Oreganata • Gnocchi Bolognese
Chicken Scarparello • Authentic Italian Desserts

SCAN FOR MENU

SOME BASICS
Reservations:	YES
Spirits:	BEER/WINE
Parking:	STREET
Outdoor Dining:	NO

AMORE RESTAURANT

180 North Lime Avenue
941-383-1111
amorelbk.com

	ITALIAN	**COST: $$$**

HOURS: Wed-Sun, 5PM to 9PM
CLOSED MONDAY & TUESDAY

WHAT TO EXPECT: Opentable Reservations • Upscale Italian Cuisine
Casual, Relaxed Atmosphere • Also A Portuguese Menu

BEST BITES: Pica-Pau de Vaca • Bacalhau Ribatenjo
Chicken Livornese • Salmon Picatta • Beef Osso Bucco

SOME BASICS

SCAN FOR MENU

Reservations:	YES
Spirits:	BEER/WINE
Parking:	LOT
Outdoor Dining:	NO

ANDREA'S

2085 Siesta Drive
941-951-9200
andreasrestaurantsrq.com

SOUTHGATE	**ITALIAN**	**COST: $$$**

HOURS: Mon-Sat, 5PM to 10PM
CLOSED SUNDAY (summer only)

WHAT TO EXPECT: Nice Wine List • Quiet Restaurant Atmosphere
Upscale Italian Cuisine • Great Special Occasion Place

BEST BITES: Polenta Concia • Tonnarelli Sunday Style
Veal Tripe Piemontese • Short Ribs Andreas

SOME BASICS

SCAN FOR MENU

Reservations:	YES
Spirits:	BEER/WINE
Parking:	LOT
Outdoor Dining:	NO

ANNA MARIA OYSTER BAR

6906 14th Street W.*
941-758-7880
oysterbar.net

BRADENTON	SEAFOOD	COST: $$

HOURS: Sun-Thur, 11AM to 9PM
Fri-Sat, 11AM to 10PM

WHAT TO EXPECT: Good For Kids • Casual, Family Atmosphere
Large Menu • Good For Groups

BEST BITES: Lots Of Raw Bar Options • Mussels Provencal
Conch Fritters • Pier Poke Bowl • Linguine With Scallops
Lobster Bisque • Gulf Grouper Sandwich • Live ME Lobster

SCAN FOR MENU

SOME BASICS

Reservations:	8 OR MORE
Spirits:	FULL BAR
Parking:	LOT
Outdoor Dining:	YES

ANNA'S DELI & SANDWICH SHOP

6535 Midnight Pass Road
941-349-4888
annasdelis.com

SIESTA KEY	DELI	COST: $

HOURS: Daily, 10:30AM to 4PM

WHAT TO EXPECT: Super Casual • Great Sandwiches (The Surfer)
Good For SK Beach To Go • Super Fast Service

BEST BITES: Sandwiches are what they do! • Surfer
Peddler • Villager • Skater • Fiesta

SCAN FOR MENU

SOME BASICS

Reservations:	NO
Spirits:	NONE
Parking:	LOT
Outdoor Dining:	NO

APOLLONIA GRILL

8235 Cooper Creek Boulevard*
941-359-4816
apolloniagrill.com

UPARK	GREEK	COST: $$

HOURS: Mon-Thur, 11:30AM to 9PM • Fri & Sat, 11:30AM to 10PM
Sunday, 11:30AM to 8:30PM

WHAT TO EXPECT: Good For Groups • Family Owned
Casual Dining • Lots Of Parking • Also A Landings Location

BEST BITES: Avegolemono Soup • Lamb Shank Osso Bucco
Seafood Salad • Spinach & Feta Flatbread • Moussaka

SOME BASICS

SCAN FOR MENU

Reservations:	YES
Spirits:	FULL BAR
Parking:	LOT
Outdoor Dining:	YES

ATHENS FAMILY RESTAURANT

2300 Bee Ridge Road
941-706-4121
athensfamilyrestaurant.business.site

	GREEK	COST: $$

HOURS: Mon-Sat, 8AM to 10PM
CLOSED SUNDAY

WHAT TO EXPECT: Casual Greek Cuisine • Good For Families
Family Owned & Operated • Lots Of Parking

BEST BITES: Greek Omelet • Bakaliaro Sandwich
Horiatiki Salad • Bifteki Platter • Baklava

SOME BASICS

SCAN FOR MENU

Reservations:	NO
Spirits:	BEER/WINE
Parking:	LOT
Outdoor Dining:	NO

ATRIA BREAD + COFFEE

4120 Lakewood Ranch Boulevard
941-751-1016
atria.cafe

LAKEWOOD RANCH	AMERICAN	COST: $$

HOURS: Cafe Open Daily, 8AM to 2:30PM
Pizza, Tue-Sat, 5PM to 8PM

WHAT TO EXPECT: Cafe By Day - Pizza By Night! • Specialty Coffee
Catering Available

BEST BITES: Hokkaido Milk Bread • Cherries Jubilee French Toast
Umami Eggs Benedict • Crispy Chicken Sandwich
Pizza • Pumpkin Madeleine

SCAN FOR MENU

SOME BASICS

Reservations:	NO
Spirits:	NONE
Parking:	LOT
Outdoor Dining:	YES

AZUL STEAK & SUSHI LOUNGE   `NEW`

1296 First Street
941-343-2122
azulsteakandsushilounge.com

DOWNTOWN	ASIAN	COST: $$$

HOURS: Daily, 5PM to 11PM

WHAT TO EXPECT: Daily Happy Hour • Nice Outdoor Dining Space
Sushi & More! • Great Place For A Meal Before The Opera

BEST BITES: Tuna Poke Nachos • Nigiri & Sashimi
Specialty Rolls • Saki Selections • Miso Sea Bass
Steaks & Chops

SCAN FOR MENU

SOME BASICS

Reservations:	YES
Spirits:	FULL BAR
Parking:	STREET
Outdoor Dining:	YES

BAKER AND WIFE

2157 Siesta Drive
941-960-1765
bakerwife.com

SOUTHGATE	AMERICAN	COST: $$

HOURS: Thur-Sat, 5PM to 9PM

WHAT TO EXPECT: Artisan Pizza • Casual Atmosphere
Lots Of Dessert Choices • Opentable Reservations

BEST BITES: Beef Carpaccio • Spicy Tuna Tartare • Caesar Salad
Pan Seared Salmon • Buckhead Beef Grilled Skirt Steak
The Meatball • Pizza! • The Bakers Burger

SOME BASICS

SCAN FOR MENU

Reservations:	YES
Spirits:	FULL BAR
Parking:	LOT
Outdoor Dining:	YES

BAR HANA

1289 North Palm Avenue
941-536-9717
barhana.com

DOWNTOWN	ASIAN	COST: $$$

HOURS: Sun-Thur, 11AM to 12M
Fri & Sat, 11AM to 2AM

WHAT TO EXPECT: Fantastic Craft Cocktails • Upscale Atmosphere
Group Dining Available • Sat & Sun Brunch

BEST BITES: Siesta Key Swizzle • Frisky Flamingo • Taro Nachos
Garlic Mazemen Noodles • Roasted Duck, Peking Style (Bao)
Wagyu + Shiitake Dumplings • Mochi Doki

SOME BASICS

SCAN FOR MENU

Reservations:	YES
Spirits:	FUL BAR
Parking:	STREET/GARAGE
Outdoor Dining:	YES

BAVARO'S PIZZA NAPOLETANA & PASTERIA
27 Fletcher Avenue
941-552-9131
bavarospizza.com

DOWNTOWN	PIZZA	COST: $$

HOURS: Sun-Thur, 5PM to 9PM
Fri & Sat, 5PM to 10PM

WHAT TO EXPECT: Casual Italian • Good For Families • Pizza!
Gluten Free Options • Opentable Reservations

BEST BITES: Pizza Napoletana • Italian Chopped Salad
Heirloom Bruschetta • Tagliatelle Bolognese • Tiramisu

SCAN FOR MENU

SOME BASICS

Reservations:	YES
Spirits:	FULL BAR
Parking:	LOT/STREET
Outdoor Dining:	YES

BAY LEAF INDIAN CUISINE   `NEW`
1092 South Tamiami Trail
941-244-0310
bayleafosprey.com

OSPREY	ASIAN	COST: $$

HOURS: Sun-Thur, 11AM to 2:30PM • Sun-Thur, 4PM to 9PM
Fri & Sat, 11AM to 2:30PM • Fri & Sat, 4PM to 9:30PM

WHAT TO EXPECT: Authentic Indian Cuisine • Catering Available
Online Ordering Available • Lots of Vegetarian Options

BEST BITES: Samosa • Creamy Butter Masala • Lamb or Goat Saag
Biriyani • Kashmiri Lamb Chops • Vindaloo
Traditional Indian Desi Thali Lunch Special

SCAN FOR MENU

SOME BASICS

Reservations:	YES
Spirits:	BEER & WINE
Parking:	LOT
Outdoor Dining:	NO

BEACH BISTRO

6600 Gulf Drive
941-778-6444
beachbistro.com

HOLMES BEACH	AMERICAN	COST: $$$$

HOURS: Daily, 5PM to 10PM

WHAT TO EXPECT: Fine Dining • Beautiful Gulf Views • Romantic
Perfect For A Special Occasion • Great Wine List & Cocktails

BEST BITES: Lobster & Shrimp Cocktail • LobsterCargots
Bistro Bouillabaisse • Maple Leaf Farms Duckling Breast

SOME BASICS

SCAN FOR MENU

Reservations: YES
Spirits: FULL BAR
Parking: VALET
Outdoor Dining: YES

BEACH HOUSE WATERFRONT RESTAURANT

200 Gulf Drive North
941-779-2222
beachhousedining.com

BRADENTON BEACH	AMERICAN	COST: $$

HOURS: Daily, 11:30AM to 10PM

WHAT TO EXPECT: Great For A Date • Florida Seafood
Nice Wine List • Lots Of Outdoor Dining Space

BEST BITES: House Smoked Fish-Dip • Gamble Farm House Salad
Seafood Gumbo • Short Rib Tacos • Key Lime Pie

SOME BASICS

SCAN FOR MENU

Reservations: NO
Spirits: FULL BAR
Parking: LOT
Outdoor Dining: YES

BEAN COFFEEHOUSE

5138 Ocean Boulevard
941-260-6400
beancoffeehouse.net

SIESTA KEY	AMERICAN	COST: $

HOURS: Daily, 7AM to 2PM

WHAT TO EXPECT: Great For A Date • Relaxed SK Coffee Shop
Basic Coffee is Self Serve • Locals Gather Here!

BEST BITES: Coffee! • Fantastic Homemade Bialys! • Fruit Smoothies
Homemade Scones • Organic Wheat Toast Sandwiches
Hot & Iced Lattes • Egg Muffin Sandwiches

MORE INFO

SOME BASICS

Reservations:	NO
Spirits:	NONE
Parking:	LOT
Outdoor Dining:	YES

BESO

30 South Lemon Avenue
941-279-2999
besosrq.com

DOWNTOWN	SPANISH	COST: $$$

HOURS: Wed-Thur, 4PM to 10PM • Fri, 4PM to 11PM
Sat, 1PM to 11PM • Sun, 1PM to 10PM • CLOSED MON & TUE

WHAT TO EXPECT: Tapas Style Dining • Great Downtown Location
Great For Groups • Vibrant & Lively Atmosphere

BEST BITES: Queso de Cabra • Pintxos Mixtos • Charcuterie
Paella • Carillada de Ternera • Pollo Ajillo • Higos
Calamares • Trucha Escabeche • Flan • Basque Cheesecake

SCAN FOR MENU

SOME BASICS

Reservations:	YES
Spirits:	FULL BAR
Parking:	STREET/GARAGE
Outdoor Dining:	NO

BEVARDI'S SALUTE! RESTAURANT

23 North Lemon Avenue
941-365-1020
salutesarasota.com

DOWNTOWN	ITALIAN	COST: $$

HOURS: Sun-Thur, 4PM to 10PM • Fri & Sat, 4PM to 11PM
Early Bird Dinner: Daily, 4pm to 6pm • CLOSED MONDAY

WHAT TO EXPECT: Live Music • In-House Catering
Opentable Reservations • Nice Outdoor Dining

BEST BITES: Salsiccia Salute • Caprese • Gnocchi Di Patate
Cotoletta Parmigiana • Branzino • Grilled Veal Chop

SOME BASICS

SCAN FOR MENU

Reservations:	YES
Spirits:	FULL BAR
Parking:	STREET/LOT
Outdoor Dining:	YES

BIG WATER FISH MARKET

6641 Midnight Pass Road
941-554-8101
bigwaterfishmarket.com

SIESTA KEY	SEAFOOD	COST: $$

HOURS: Mon-Sat, 11AM to 9PM
Sunday, 12PM to 8PM

WHAT TO EXPECT: Fresh Fish Market • Casual Dining
SK South Bridge Location • Key Lime Pie!

BEST BITES: Conch Cakes • "Jacks" Fish Stew • Hogfish
Grouper Reuben • Stone Crab (in season) • Key Lime Pie

SOME BASICS

SCAN FOR MENU

Reservations:	NO
Spirits:	BEER/WINE
Parking:	LOT
Outdoor Dining:	NO

BIJOU GARDEN CAFÉ

1287 First Street
941-366-8111
bijoucafe.net

DOWNTOWN	AMERICAN	COST: $$$

HOURS: Tue-Thur, 5PM to 9PM • Fri & Sat, 5PM to 10PM
CLOSED SUNDAY & MONDAY

WHAT TO EXPECT: Great For A Date • Excellent Wine List
Opentable Reservations • Private Dining Program

BEST BITES: Truffle Butternut Squash Soup • Escargot Bourguignon
Open Faced Lobster Ravioli • Roasted Half Peking Duck
Pommes Gratin Dauphinois • Maple Bread Pudding

SCAN FOR MENU

SOME BASICS

Reservations:	YES
Spirits:	FULL BAR
Parking:	VALET
Outdoor Dining:	YES

BIRDROCK TACO SHACK

1213 13th Avenue W
941-545-9966
birdrocktacoshack.com

BRADENTON	MEXICAN	COST: $$$

HOURS: Tue-Sat, 12PM to 9PM
CLOSED SUNDAY & MONDAY

WHAT TO EXPECT: Funky Village of the Arts Taco Shop • LIVE MUSIC
Vegan & Vegetarian Options • Special Events

BEST BITES: Beef Short Rib Taco • Pork Tamale • Avocado Smash
Pork Belly Pastor Taco • Chicken Tinga Burrito
Lobster Nachos Queso • Goat Cheese Caprese Taco

MORE INFO

SOME BASICS

Reservations:	NO
Spirits:	BEER & WINE
Parking:	STREET
Outdoor Dining:	YES

BLU KOUZINA

25 North Boulevard of Presidents
941-388-2619
blukouzina.com/US

ST. ARMANDS	GREEK	COST: $$$

HOURS: Daily, 11:30AM to 8:30PM

WHAT TO EXPECT: Nice Wine List • Real Greek Cuisine
Opentable Reservations • Many Small Plate Appetizers

BEST BITES: Taramosalata • Dolmades • Keftedes
Kalamaki Souvlaki • Roast Lemon Chicken
Lamb Kabob • Mousaka • Octopus • Pastitsio

SOME BASICS

SCAN FOR MENU

Reservations:	YES
Spirits:	BEER/WINE
Parking:	STREET
Outdoor Dining:	YES

BLUE KOI

3801 McIntosh Road
941-388-7738
bluekoisushi.com

	SUSHI	COST: $$

HOURS: LUNCH: Wed-Fri, 11:30AM to 1:30PM • CLOSED SUNDAY
DINNER: Mon-Thur, 5PM to 9PM • Fri & Sat, 4PM to 9PM

WHAT TO EXPECT: Carryout & Delivery Only • Super Creative Sushi
Catering Available • Online Ordering

INSIDER TIP: Sushi Combo • Family Platter • Poke Bowls
Seared Ahi Tuna Salad • Salmon Bowl • Miso Soup

SOME BASICS

SCAN FOR MENU

Reservations:	NO
Spirits:	NONE
Parking:	LOT
Outdoor Dining:	NO

BLVD CAFE
1580 Boulevard of the Arts
941-203-8102
blvdcafesrq.com

ROSEMARY DIST.	AMERICAN	COST: $$

HOURS: Wed-Mon, 7AM to 5PM
CLOSED TUESDAY

WHAT TO EXPECT: Super Casual • Breakfast & Lunch Only
Lots Of Parking • Great Sidewalk Seating

INSIDER TIP: Braided Brioche French Toast • French Onion Soup
Seared Yellowfin Tuna Salad • Croque Monsieur
Salmon Bagel • Masala Chai Tea

SCAN FOR MENU

SOME BASICS

Reservations:	NO
Spirits:	NONE
Parking:	STREET
Outdoor Dining:	YES

BOCA SARASOTA
19 South Lemon Avenue
941-256-3565
bocasarasota.com

DOWNTOWN	AMERICAN	COST: $$

HOURS: Mon-Fri, 11AM to 10PM • Sat, 10AM to 11PM
Sun, 10AM to 10PM

WHAT TO EXPECT: Sat & Sun Brunch • Online Reservations
Classic Cocktails • Craft Beer Selections

BEST BITES: Skirt Steak • 60 Spiced Chicken • OMG Burger
Smoked Fish Dip • Flatbreads! • Grilled Caesar
Chopped Salad • Guava Cheesecake • Key Lime Jar

SCAN FOR MENU

SOME BASICS

Reservations:	YES
Spirits:	FULL BAR
Parking:	STREET
Outdoor Dining:	YES

BOHEMIOS WINE & BEER TAPAS BAR

3246 Clark Road
941-260-9784
srqbohemios.com

	TAPAS	COST: $$

HOURS: Mon-Thur, 4PM to 10PM • Fri & Sat, 4PM to 12AM
CLOSED SUNDAY

WHAT TO EXPECT: Good Sized Wine List • Great Small Plate Dishes
Intimate Dining Atmosphere • Lots Of Parking

BEST BITES: Caprese Bruschetta • Chistorra • Gamba Scampi
Shrimp & Chorizo Stew • Lamb Lollipops • Ahi Tuna
Bohemios Churrasco • Tres Leches • Lava Cake

SOME BASICS

SCAN FOR MENU

Reservations:	YES
Spirits:	BEER/WINE
Parking:	LOT
Outdoor Dining:	NO

BONJOUR FRENCH CAFÉ

5214 Ocean Boulevard
941-346-0600
bonjourfrenchcafe.com

SIESTA KEY	FRENCH	COST: $$

HOURS: Daily, 7:30AM to 2:30PM

WHAT TO EXPECT: Super Casual • Great Outdoor Dining
Great Crepes!

BEST BITES: Eggs Benedict • Crepes • Belgian Waffles
Omelet "La Parisienne" • Croissants • Quiche Lorraine
Baguette Sandwiches • Nicoise Salad • Sea Ocean Salad

SOME BASICS

SCAN FOR MENU

Reservations:	NO
Spirits:	BEER/WINE
Parking:	STREET
Outdoor Dining:	YES

All Faiths Food Bank:
Addressing Food Insecurity Today,
Working To End Hunger Forever
By Sandra Frank, CEO

As you take the time to enjoy this publication and make plans to dine out – or order in – from some of the wonderful restaurants featured in these pages, you might not realize that many of our neighbors don't have enough to eat.

Sarasota is one of the richest counties in the state, yet nearly 50% of the kids in our schools rely on the free and reduced meal program. Thousands of area families are worried about empty refrigerators and barren cupboards. Parents are skipping meals so their children can eat.

And the first place our neighbors turn for help is All Faiths Food Bank – the only food bank and largest hunger relief organization in Sarasota and DeSoto counties.

All Faiths Food Bank provides millions of meals each year and works to end hunger – forever – by addressing the root causes of food insecurity and helping families achieve self-sufficiency. In 2022, All Faiths Food Bank fed nearly 62,000 individuals, distributed nearly 21 million pounds of food equating to 18 million meals, and put more than $4 million back into the community through its benefits assistance programs.

The key program areas for All Faiths Food Bank are: childhood hunger (Campaign Against Summer Hunger, the BackPack Program, school and family pantry programs); food distribution (mobile pantries, produce program, a veterans pantry, and through partner agencies); hunger and health (food insecurity screening programs); benefits assistance (SNAP, Medicaid, tax preparation, rent assistance, and Social Security disability benefits); and rural hunger (DeSoto County Food & Resource Center).

Hunger is a health issue and All Faiths has reinvented itself to establish the infrastructure and processes that incorporate community health principles. All Faiths has established partnerships with our region's leading healthcare organizations and nonprofit partners to screen more than 66,000 people for food insecurity, offer nutrition assistance, and refer families for additional social services.

All Faiths is also dedicated to raising awareness and engaging an even broader community to influence policy-making regarding hunger. The organization's new strategic plan emphasizes a deeper investment in non-traditional food bank partnerships to create a region-wide movement that recognizes the role everyone – policy-makers, social service networks, funders, donors, and the larger community – can play to end hunger.

Additionally, All Faiths is one of the lead emergency response organizations at the local and state level. The organization stands ready even before a natural disaster strikes, responding to emergency needs locally as well as supporting its sister food banks throughout the state.

The community has long been responsive to the cause: All Faiths is honored to have one of the most robust volunteer bases in our area. In 2022, more than 3,300 volunteers contributed over 48,000 volunteer hours to support the organization's work and mission of ending hunger. The organization's "people first" culture also makes it a place where employees can thrive and advance: in 2023, All Faiths was named one of the Top 100 Best Companies To Work For in Florida by Florida Trend and the HR Florida State Council.

When people are fed, futures are nourished. With your donation of money, food, and/or time, you will help to open endless possibilities for people to thrive.

To learn how you can be a "hunger hero" to our neighbors in need, visit allfaithsfoodbank.org.

All Faiths Food Bank is the only food bank and largest hunger relief organization in Sarasota and DeSoto counties. A member of Feeding America, the organization provides millions of meals each year through robust programs and partnerships with charitable organizations in the community and operates a roster

MORE INFO

of innovative direct service programs that not only solve the immediate problem of hunger but strive to end hunger by helping families and individuals gain long-term food security, better health outcomes, and self-sufficiency. All Faiths Food Bank is rated 4-stars by Charity Navigator.

THE BREAKFAST COMPANY
7246 55th Avenue E.
941-201-6002
thebreakfastcompanyfl.com

BRADENTON	AMERICAN	COST: $$

HOURS: Tues-Sun, 7AM to 2PM
CLOSED MONDAY

WHAT TO EXPECT: Breakfast & Lunch Only • Local Ingredients
Good For Families • Also a Great Landings Location!

BEST BITES: Large Omelet Selection • Skillet Bowls
Terri's Famous Quiche • Strawberry Nutella French Toast
Scratch-Made Soups • California Cobb Salad

SCAN FOR MENU

SOME BASICS

Reservations:	NO
Spirits:	NONE
Parking:	LOT
Outdoor Dining:	YES

THE BREAKFAST HOUSE

1817 Fruitville Road
941-366-6860
sarasotabreakfasthouse.com

DOWNTOWN	AMERICAN	COST: $$

HOURS: Wed-Sun, 8AM to 2PM
CLOSED MONDAY & TUESDAY

WHAT TO EXPECT: Charming Atmosphere • Breakfast & Lunch
Great Omelets • Eclectic

BEST BITES: Lots Of Omelet Selections • Belgian Waffles
Lavender Stuffed Blueberry Pancakes • Vegan Skillet

SOME BASICS

SCAN FOR INFO

Reservations:	NO
Spirits:	NONE
Parking:	LOT
Outdoor Dining:	YES

BREWBURGERS PUB & GRILL

370 Commercial Court
941-484-2337
brewburgers.com

VENICE	AMERICAN	COST: $$

HOURS: Daily, 11AM to 10PM

WHAT TO EXPECT: Super Casual • Try Brewburgers Back Porch!
"Icy Cold" Craft Beer Selection • Growler Fill Station

BEST BITES: Homemade "Saratoga" Chips • Lots of Burgers!!
Brew House Salad • Cheeseburger Club • Chili Fries
Tammy's Tot Basket • Brewburgers Cuban

SOME BASICS

SCAN FOR MENU

Reservations:	NO
Spirits:	BEER/WINE
Parking:	LOT
Outdoor Dining:	NO

BRICK'S SMOKED MEATS

1528 State Street
941-993-1435
brickssmokedmeats.com

DOWNTOWN	BBQ	COST: $$

HOURS: Sun-Thur, 11AM to 10PM • Friday, 11AM to 11PM
Saturday, 10AM to 1PM

WHAT TO EXPECT: State Street Garage • Bbq, Bbq, Bbq
Good Local Beer List • Upbeat Atmosphere • Catering

BEST BITES: Pulled Pork • USDA Prime Brisket • St. Louis Ribs
Chicken Fried Chicken • Smoked Wings • Brisket Chili
Bacon Burnt Ends Tacos • State Street Corn

SCAN FOR MENU

SOME BASICS

Reservations:	NO
Spirits:	FULL BAR
Parking:	STREET/GARAGE
Outdoor Dining:	YES

BRINE SEAFOOD & RAW BAR

2250 Gulf Gate Drive
941-404-5639
BrineSarasota.com

GULF GATE	SEAFOOD	COST: $$

HOURS: Sun-Thur, 11AM to 10PM
Fri & Sat, 11AM to 11PM

WHAT TO EXPECT: Raw Bar • Northeastern Style Seafood
Busy During Season • Vibrant Atmosphere

BEST BITES: Oysters on the Half Shell • Charred Octopus
Cream of Crab Soup • Jumbo Lump Crab Cakes
Pan Seared Snapper • Lobster Roll • Crab Cake Sandwich

SCAN FOR MENU

SOME BASICS

Reservations:	YES
Spirits:	FULL BAR
Parking:	LOT/STREET
Outdoor Dining:	YES

BUSHIDO IZAYAKI

3688 Webber Steet
941-217-5635
bushidosushisrq.com

	SUSHI	COST: $$

HOURS: Mon-Sat, 4PM to 9PM
CLOSED SUNDAY

WHAT TO EXPECT: Japanese Cuisine • Sushi • Casual Atmosphere
Good For Families

BEST BITES: Spicy Seafood Miso Soup • Hawaii Martini
Sashimi & Nigiri • Bushido Signature Rolls!
Teryiaki & Tempura Dishes

SOME BASICS

SCAN FOR MENU

Reservations:	YES
Spirits:	BEER & WINE
Parking:	LOT
Outdoor Dining:	NO

BUTTERMILK HANDCRAFTED FOOD

5520 Palmer Boulevard
941-487-8949

SOUTH TRAIL	ITALIAN	COST: $$

HOURS: Tues-Fri, 7AM to 1PM • Sat, 8AM to 1PM
CLOSED SUNDAY & MONDAY

WHAT TO EXPECT: Great Homemade Baked Goods • Small Menu
Counter Service Only

BEST BITES: Specialty Coffee • Homemade Cookies
Biscuit Sandwiches • Avocado Toast • Espresso

SOME BASICS

SCAN FOR INFO

Reservations:	NO
Spirits:	NONE
Parking:	LOT
Outdoor Dining:	YES

CAFÉ BARBOSSO

5501 Palmer Crossing Circle
941-922-7999
cafebarbosso.com

| PALMER CROSSING | ITALIAN | COST: $$ |

HOURS: Tues-Sun, 4PM to 9PM
CLOSED MONDAY

WHAT TO EXPECT: Authentic NYC Italian • Casual Dining
Fun Dining Experience • Good For Groups

BEST BITES: Mozzarella in Carrozza • Fresh Mozzarella Caprese
Grandma's Spaghettini 'n Meatballs • Seafood Fra Diavolo
Chicken Marsala or Piccata • Personal Pizzas!

SCAN FOR MENU

SOME BASICS

Reservations:	YES
Spirits:	FULL BAR
Parking:	LOT
Outdoor Dining:	YES

CAFÉ EPICURE

1298 North Palm Avenue
941-366-5648
cafeepicure.com

| DOWNTOWN | ITALIAN | COST: $$ |

HOURS: Daily, 11:45AM to 10:30PM

WHAT TO EXPECT: Great For A Date • Wood Fired Pizza
Casual Italian Fare • Palm Avenue Garage

BEST BITES: Salumeria - Formaggi & Salumi • Tartare Di Tonni
Pappardelle Bolognese • Pasta E Fagioli
Milanese Di Pollo • Pizza • Filetto Di Salmone

SCAN FOR MENU

SOME BASICS

Reservations:	YES
Spirits:	FULL BAR
Parking:	STREET/PALM GARAGE
Outdoor Dining:	YES

CAFÉ GABBIANO

5104 Ocean Boulevard
941-349-1423
cafegabbiano.com

SIESTA KEY	ITALIAN	COST: $$$

HOURS: Daily, 5PM to 10PM

WHAT TO EXPECT: Great Wine List • Siesta Village Location
Lots Of Parking • Opentable Reservations • Nightly Specials

BEST BITES: Formaggi & Salumi Plate • Bruschetta di Ischia
The Poached Pear • Costolette di Vitello • Ossobuco Ravioli
Branzino • Lasagne Bolognese

SOME BASICS

SCAN FOR MENU

Reservations:	YES
Spirits:	FULL BAR
Parking:	LOT
Outdoor Dining:	YES

CAFÉ L'EUROPE

431 St. Armands Circle
941-388-4415
cafeleurope.net

ST. ARMANDS	EUROPEAN	COST: $$$

HOURS: Tues-Sun, 11AM to 9PM
CLOSED MONDAY

WHAT TO EXPECT: Weekend Brunch • Special Wine Dinners
Fine Dining Since 1973 • Newly Remodeled Bar Area

BEST BITES: Escargot • Oysters Rockefeller • French Onion Gratinee
Wedge Salad • Australian Rack of Lamb • French Grouper
Osso Bucco • Veal Piccata

SOME BASICS

SCAN FOR MENU

Reservations:	YES
Spirits:	FULL BAR
Parking:	VALET/STREET
Outdoor Dining:	YES

CAFE VENICE

101 W Venice Avenue
941-484-1855
cafevenicerestaurantandbar.com

VENICE	ECLECTIC	COST: $$$

HOURS: Tues-Sat, 11:30AM to 9PM
CLOSED SUNDAY & MONDAY

WHAT TO EXPECT: Super Eclectic Menu • LIVE Music
Catering Available • Downtown Venice Location

BEST BITES: Seared Scallops • Café Venice Mussels • Venice Caesar
Venice Caprese • Bouillabaisse • Crispy Roasted Duck
Pork Osso Bucco • Famous Crispy Spinach

SCAN FOR MENU

SOME BASICS

Reservations:	YES
Spirits:	FULL BAR
Parking:	STREET
Outdoor Dining:	YES

CAPO PAZZO

NEW

2053 Reynolds Street
941-487-8677
capopazzo.com

SOUTH TRAIL	ITALIAN	COST: $$

HOURS: Mon, Wed, Thur, Sun, 11AM to 9PM
Fri & Sat, 11AM to 10PM • CLOSED TUESDAY

WHAT TO EXPECT: Casual Italian Cuisine • Good For Families
Fantastic NY Style Pizza!!

BEST BITES: Red & White Pizza Styles • Baked Ziti Bites • Farro Salad
Arancini • Potato Gnocchi • Penne Alla Vodka
Capo Garlic Knots

SCAN FOR MENU

SOME BASICS

Reservations:	YES
Spirits:	BEER & WINE
Parking:	LOT
Outdoor Dining:	NO

CAPTAIN CURT'S CRAB & OYSTER BAR

1200 Old Stickney Point Road
941-349-3885
captaincurts.com

SIESTA KEY	SEAFOOD	COST: $$

HOURS: Daily, 11AM to 2AM

WHAT TO EXPECT: Good For Kids • Super Casual • Lots Of Seafood
Ohio State Football HQ • Live Music • "Sniki Tiki"

BEST BITES: Award Winning Clam Chowder • Grouper Sandwich
Snow Crab Platter • Buffalo Wings! • Stone Crab (in season)
Alaskan Fish and Chips • Crab Cake Sandwich

SOME BASICS

SCAN FOR MENU

Reservations:	NO
Spirits:	FULL BAR
Parking:	LOT
Outdoor Dining:	YES

CASA MASA

NEW

2773 Bee Ridge Road
941-922-8226
islandhousetaqueria.com

	MEXICAN	COST: $$

HOURS: Daily, 11AM to 10PM

WHAT TO EXPECT: Great Tacos! • Super Casual Atmosphere
Authentic Al Pastor Tacos • Good Craft Beer Selection

BEST BITES: Pork Al Pastor • Birria • Pork Belly
Duck Carnitas • Burritos & Bowls
Try a Mexican Coke!

SOME BASICS

SCAN FOR MENU

Reservations:	NO
Spirits:	BEER/WINE
Parking:	LOT
Outdoor Dining:	YES

CASEY KEY FISH HOUSE
801 Blackburn Point Road
941-966-1901
caseykeyfishhouse.com

OSPREY	SEAFOOD	COST: $$

HOURS: Daily, 11:30AM to 9PM

WHAT TO EXPECT: Vacation Atmosphere • Local Seafood
Boat Docks • Old Florida Feel • Live Music

BEST BITES: U Peel U Eat Shrimp • New England Clam Chowder
Grouper Sandwich • Shrimp Scampi • Seafood Pasta
Diver Scallops with Citrus Sauce • Key Lime Pie

SCAN FOR MENU

SOME BASICS
Reservations:	NO
Spirits:	FULL BAR
Parking:	LOT
Outdoor Dining:	YES

CASSARIANO
313 West Venice Avenue*
941-786-1000
cassariano.com

VENICE	ITALIAN	COST: $$$

HOURS: Lunch - Mon-Sat, From 11AM
Dinner - Nightly

WHAT TO EXPECT: Contemporary Italian Cuisine • Also a LWR location
Special Event Space Available • Wine Dinners

BEST BITES: Burrata con Prosciutto • Arancino di Riso
Tagliatelle alla Rustica • Gnocchi Sorrento
Veal Chop alla Caprese • Salmone ai Ferri

SCAN FOR MENU

SOME BASICS
Reservations:	YES
Spirits:	FULL BAR
Parking:	STREET
Outdoor Dining:	NO

CARAGIULOS

69 South Palm Avenue
941-951-0866
caragiulos.com

DOWNTOWN	ITALIAN	COST: $$

HOURS: Sun-Thur, 4:30PM to 9:30PM
Fri & Sat, 4:30PM to 10:30PM

WHAT TO EXPECT: Casual Dining • Palm Ave. Gallery District
Good For Kids • Good For Groups

BEST BITES: Roman Artichokes • Salumi e Formaggi Board
Roasted Beet & Avocado Salad • Chopped 1989 Salad
Picatta Style Veal • Pizza! • Local Grouper

SOME BASICS

SCAN FOR MENU

Reservations:	YES
Spirits:	FULL BAR
Parking:	STREET/VALET
Outdoor Dining:	YES

C'EST LA VIE!

1553 Main Street
941-906-9575
cestlaviesarasota.com

DOWNTOWN	FRENCH	COST: $$

HOURS: Mon-Wed, 7:30AM to 6PM • Thur-Sat, 7:30AM to 10PM
Sunday, 8:30AM to 5PM

WHAT TO EXPECT: Outdoor Tables • Relaxed Cafe Dining
Fantastic Bakery • Opentable Reservations

BEST BITES: Le Petit Déjeuner • Chocolate Croissant • Crepes
Baguette Sandwiches • Omelets • Quiche Lorraine
Croq' Madame • Parisienne Salad

SOME BASICS

SCAN FOR MENU

Reservations:	YES
Spirits:	BEER/WINE
Parking:	STREET
Outdoor Dining:	YES

CHA CHA COCONUTS TROPICAL BAR

417 St. Armands Circle
941-388-3300
chacha-coconuts.com

ST. ARMANDS	AMERICAN	COST: $$

HOURS: Sun-Thur, 11AM to 10PM
Fri & Sat, 11AM to 11PM

WHAT TO EXPECT: Good For Kids • Lot Of Outdoor Tables
Bustling Atmosphere • LIVE Music

BEST BITES: Grouper Bites • Calypso Chicken Wings
Peel & Eat Shrimp • Tony Salad • Grouper Tacos
Cuban Mixed Sandwich • Divi Divi Burger • Key Lime Pie

SCAN FOR MENU

SOME BASICS

Reservations:	NO
Spirits:	FULL BAR
Parking:	STREET/GARAGE/VALET
Outdoor Dining:	YES

THE CHATEAU SARASOTA

535 13th Street W.
941-226-0110
chateau-13.com

SOUTH TRAIL	EUROPEAN	COST: $$$

HOURS: Tues-Sun, 3PM to close • Sunday Brunch, 11AM to 3PM
CLOSED MONDAY

WHAT TO EXPECT: • Great Wine List • Chefs Table Tasting Menu
Upscale Dining Experience • Nice Special Occasion Dining

BEST BITES: Charcuterie & Cheese Board • Seafood Tower
Rabbit Fricassee • Duck à l'Orange • Airline Chicken
Escargot • Chateau Caesar Salad

SCAN FOR MENU

SOME BASICS

Reservations:	YES
Spirits:	FULL BAR
Parking:	VALET
Outdoor Dining:	NO

CHAZ 51 STEAKHOUSE

`NEW`

549 US-41(Bypass North)
941-484-6200
chaz51steakhouse.com

VENICE	STEAKHOUSE	COST: $$$

HOURS: Sun-Thur, 4PM to 9PM • Fri & Sat, 4PM to 9:30PM
Happy Hour Daily

WHAT TO EXPECT: Prime Angus Beef • Wine Tastings
Private Dining Available • Craft Cocktails

BEST BITES: Blue Crab Martini • Mussels Parisienne
Iceberg Wedge BLT • USDA Prime NY Strip Steak
Panko Crusted Gulf Grouper • Sautéed Spinach with Garlic

SOME BASICS

SCAN FOR MENU

Reservations:	YES
Spirits:	FULL BAR
Parking:	LOT
Outdoor Dining:	NO

CHIANTI RISTORANTE ITALIANO

3900 Clark Road
941-952-3186
chiantisarasota.com

	ITALIAN	COST: $$$

HOURS: Tues-Sat, 4PM to 9PM • Sunday, 4PM to 9PM
CLOSED MONDAY

WHAT TO EXPECT: "Authentic Taste of Tuscany" • LIVE Music
Private Events • Daily Chef Specials

BEST BITES: Carpaccio Di Manza • Pinsa Romana • Polpette •
Spaghetti Alla Carbonara • Pere E Gorgonzola
Salmon Piccata • Sogliola Capri

SOME BASICS

SCAN FOR MENU

Reservations:	YES
Spirits:	FULL BAR
Parking:	LOT
Outdoor Dining:	NO

CIRCO

1435 2nd Street
941-253-0978
circosrq.com

DOWNTOWN	MEXICAN	COST: $$

HOURS: Mon, 4PM to 10PM • Tue, 11AM to 9PM • Sun, 12PM to 9PM
Wed-Thur, 9PM to 10PM • Fri & Sat, 12PM to 10PM

WHAT TO EXPECT: Super Casual • "Taco & Bourbon Joint"
Good For A Group • Catering Available

BEST BITES: Chips & Elote Corn Salsa • Tijuana Salad
Tamale Cake • Picnic Chicken Tacos • Walking Taco
Mongolian Beef Taco • Ahi Poke Taco

SCAN FOR MENU

SOME BASICS

Reservations:	NO
Spirits:	FULL BAR
Parking:	STREET/GARAGE
Outdoor Dining:	YES

CLASICO ITALIAN CHOPHOUSE

1341 Main Street
941-957-0700
clasicosrq.com

DOWNTOWN	ITALIAN	COST: $$

HOURS: Mon & Tue, 11:30AM to 11PM • Wed-Fri, 11:30AM to 12AM
Sat, 10AM to 12AM • Sun, 10AM to 11PM

WHAT TO EXPECT: Great For A Date • Live Music • Energetic Scene
Sat. & Sun. Brunch • Happy Hour Specials

BEST BITES: Tomato Bruschetta • Beef Carpaccio • Raw Bar
Gorgonzola Steak Gnocchi • Braised Short Rib
Italian Chopped Salad • Pizza!

SCAN FOR MENU

SOME BASICS

Reservations:	YES
Spirits:	FULL BAR
Parking:	STREET/PALM GARAGE
Outdoor Dining:	YES

THE COLUMBIA RESTAURANT

411 St. Armands Circle
941-388-3987
columbiarestaurant.com

ST. ARMANDS	CUBAN/SPANISH	COST: $$$

HOURS: Sun-Thur, 11AM to 9PM
Fri & Sat, 11AM to 10PM

WHAT TO EXPECT: Fantastic Sangria • Excellent Service
Opentable Reservations • Very Busy In Season

BEST BITES: 1905 Salad • Cuban Black Bean Soup • Cuban Sandwich
Empanadas de Picadillo • Roast Pork "a la Cubana"
Snapper a la Rusa • Flan

SOME BASICS

SCAN FOR MENU

Reservations:	YES
Spirits:	FULL BAR
Parking:	STREET/GARAGE
Outdoor Dining:	YES

CONNORS STEAKHOUSE

3501 South Tamiami Trail
941-260-3232
connorsrestaurant.com

SOUTHGATE	STEAKHOUSE	COST: $$$

HOURS: Sun-Thur, 11AM to 10PM
Fri & Sat, 11AM to 11PM

WHAT TO EXPECT: Lots Of Parking • Large Menu
Lots Of Wines By The Glass • Opentable Reservations

BEST BITES: Jumbo Shrimp Cocktail • Truffled Deviled Eggs
Lobster Crab Bisque • Espresso Rub Ribeye
Chilean Sea Bass Oscar • Chicken Piccata

SOME BASICS

SCAN FOR MENU

Reservations:	YES
Spirits:	FULL BAR
Parking:	LOT/VALET
Outdoor Dining:	YES

Mocktails are Making Their Mark on Sarasota

By Lauren Jackson

As many Americans are moving away from alcoholic beverages and turning toward healthy and less headache-inducing drinks, the bar culture has evolved. And Sarasota is keeping in step with the trend, with many bars and restaurants tailoring their drink lists to cater to those who are sober and others who might just be "sober curious."

At Meliora in Southside Village, the bartending team stays busy tinkering with infusions and botanicals to keep zero-octane drinks exciting. And the extensive wine list even includes non-alcoholic wines that actually taste fantastic, especially the Lyre's Classico Sparkling, which could easily be mistaken for prosecco.

99 Bottles in downtown Sarasota is also no stranger to non-alcoholic wines, with an extensive list of offerings for its many guests who gather for happy hour. Their non-alcoholic beer list is one to behold as well. At one recent visit, the Mango Cart beer from Golden Road Brewing had a round mango nose with crisp acidity followed by more mango creeping through in its finish.

For more mango fun, try the mango lassi at Turmeric. The traditional Indian yogurt-based drink almost sips like a milkshake and is perfect when you're looking for a sweet treat. But if you would rather something a little lighter, the "coconut cooler" will leave you craving sip after sip of its coconut water and orange juice-based goodness.

While the St. Armands Circle restaurant Tommy Bahama may not be headquartered in Sarasota, the corporate restaurant chain has remained in our hearts through its willingness to shake up the menu every now and again. The mocktail list is no exception and is sublime. The "pain chiller" is a clever riff on the classic painkiller cocktail that has plenty of coconut and pineapple with none of the morning-after consequences. Or opt for a cranberry refresher made with cranberry, ginger beer, and mint while watching the crowds from the upstairs patio barstools.

Back in downtown Sarasota, State Street Eating House + Cocktails takes a more spur-of-the-moment approach. Instead of offering a set mocktail list, they ask their guests to tell them the flavor profile they're looking for. Sweet and smoky, bright and citrusy, or even whiskey-evoking are excellent descriptors when speaking with its skilled bartenders. Or ask them to surprise you if you're feeling indecisive. You won't be disappointed.

But sometimes, you may not be looking for a bar environment while enjoying a sip of something wonderful. For a full, non-alcoholic experience, try Summer Tap Juice Bar instead. There, owner Galina Naguibine and her team will press fresh fruit into an infinite array of flavor combinations based on your every whim. The "savory tomato" is a great bloody Mary replacement, and the "seasonal star fruit" is the stuff of dreams.

Although trends come and go, it's clear that the mocktail movement is here to stay. No matter your reasons for turning toward an alcohol-free alternative, the choices are now seemingly endless, and we are thankful.

Lauren Jackson is the Eat & Drink Editor for Sarasota Magazine. As a Sarasota native, she knows where to find the hidden gems in town. Although she isn't great at keeping a secret, she is good at finding the next hot spot.

Read More of Lauren Jackson's Work

THE COTTAGE
153 Avenida Messina
941-312-9300
cottagesiestakey.com

SIESTA KEY	AMERICAN	COST: $$

HOURS: Sun-Thur, 11AM to 10PM
Fri & Sat, 11AM to 11PM

WHAT TO EXPECT: Tapas • Siesta Village • Outdoor Dining
Vacation Atmosphere • Nice Craft Beer Selection

BEST BITES: Grouper Sandwich • Billionaire Burger
Lobster Bisque • Tuna Tacoshimi • Black Mussels
Beef Short Ribs • Siesta Seafood Scampi

SCAN FOR MENU

SOME BASICS

Reservations:	NO
Spirits:	FULL BAR
Parking:	STREET/VALET
Outdoor Dining:	YES

CRAB & FIN
420 St. Armands Circle
941-388-3964
crabfinrestaurant.com

ST. ARMANDS	SEAFOOD	COST: $$$

HOURS: Sun-Thur, 11:30AM to 9PM
Fri & Sat, 11:30AM to 9:30PM

WHAT TO EXPECT: Great For A Date • Sunday Brunch
Online Reservations • Early Dining Options

BEST BITES: Norwegian Sea Opilio Snow Crab • Raw Bar
Whole Local Mangrove Snapper • Alaskan Halibut
Gazpacho • Prime Butcher's Block Pork Ribeye

SCAN FOR MENU

SOME BASICS

Reservations:	YES
Spirits:	FULL BAR
Parking:	STREET/LOT
Outdoor Dining:	YES

THE CROW'S NEST

1968 Tarpon Center Drive
941-484-9551
crowsnest-venice.com

VENICE	SEAFOOD	COST: $$

HOURS: Lunch: Daily, 11:30AM to 3PM
Sun-Thur, 4:30PM to 9PM • Fri & Sat, 4:30PM to 9:30PM

WHAT TO EXPECT: Water View • Good Wine List
Opentable Reservations

BEST BITES: Raw Bar • Classic Shrimp Cocktail • Seafood Tower
Seafood Bisque • Oysters Rockefeller • Escargots
Bouillabaisse • 12oz Ribeye • Chicken Piccata

SOME BASICS

SCAN FOR MENU

Reservations:	YES
Spirits:	FULL BAR
Parking:	LOT
Outdoor Dining:	YES

CURRY STATION

3550 Clark Road
941-924-7222
currystation.net

	INDIAN	COST: $$

HOURS: Lunch Buffet: Mon-Sat, 11:30AM to 2:30PM
Dinner: Mon-Sat, 5PM to 9:30PM • CLOSED SUNDAY

WHAT TO EXPECT: Huge Indian Menu • Lots Of Curries
A Dozen Naan And Other Breads • Online Reservations

BEST BITES: Veg Samosa • Aloo Tikki Chat • Tandoor Chicken Tikka
Butter Chicken • Chicken Korma • Shrimp Biryani
Lamb Vindaloo • Seafood Curry • Chana Masala

SOME BASICS

SCAN FOR MENU

Reservations:	YES
Spirits:	BEER/WINE
Parking:	LOT
Outdoor Dining:	NO

DAIQUIRI DECK RAW BAR

5250 Ocean Boulevard*
941-349-8697
daiquirideck.com

SIESTA KEY	AMERICAN	COST: $$

HOURS: Sun-Thur, 11AM to 11PM
Fri & Sat, 11AM to 1AM

WHAT TO EXPECT: Great After Beach Stop • Super Casual
Good For Families • Dozens Of Frozen Daiquiri Flavors!

BEST BITES: Siesta Fiesta Platter • Smoked Fish Dip
Peel And Eat Shrimp • Crab Cake BLT
Key West Mahi Salad • Lobster Mac and Cheese

SCAN FOR MENU

SOME BASICS

Reservations:	NO
Spirits:	FULL BAR
Parking:	STREET
Outdoor Dining:	YES

DARUMA JAPANESE STEAK HOUSE

5459 Fruitville Road*
941-342-6600
darumarestaurant.com

FRUITVILLE RD	ASIAN	COST: $$

HOURS: Daily, 5PM to 10PM

WHAT TO EXPECT: Fun Date Night • Good For Kids • Great For Groups
Private Parties

BEST BITES: Gyoza • Negamaki • DaRuMa Teppan Combinations
Sushi • Shrimp Tempura • YoYo Shrimp
Warm & Cold Sake Choices

SCAN FOR MENU

SOME BASICS

Reservations:	YES
Spirits:	FULL BAR
Parking:	LOT
Outdoor Dining:	NO

DEEP LAGOON SEAFOOD & OYSTER HOUSE   `NEW`

482 Blackburn Point Road
941-770-3337
deeplagoon.com

OSPREY	AMERICAN	COST: $$$

HOURS: Daily, 11AM to 10PM

WHAT TO EXPECT: FL Outdoor Dining • Great Water Views
11-4 "Light Lunch" Menu

BEST BITES: Oysters Rockefeller • Scallop Ceviche
Big Chill Seafood Tower • Lobster Bisque • Stuffed Hogfish
Seared Ahi Tuna Salad • Raw Bar • Bone-In Ribeye

SOME BASICS

SCAN FOR MENU

Reservations:	YES
Spirits:	FULL BAR
Parking:	LOT
Outdoor Dining:	YES

DER DUTCHMAN

3713 Bahia Vista Street
941-955-8007
dhgroup.com

PINECRAFT	AMISH	COST: $$

HOURS: Mon-Sat, 7AM to 8PM
CLOSED SUNDAY

WHAT TO EXPECT: Good For Kids • Best Buffet in the U.S.
Home Cooking • Great Pie • Groups Welcome

BEST BITES: Roast Beef, Turkey, or Meatloaf Manhattan
Homemade Soups • Broasted Chicken • Pie!
Breakfast, Lunch & Dinner Buffet

SOME BASICS

SCAN FOR MENU

Reservations:	NO
Spirits:	NONE
Parking:	LOT
Outdoor Dining:	NO

DIM SUM KING

8194 Tourist Center Drive
941-306-5848
dimsumsarasota.com

LAKEWOOD RANCH	ASIAN	COST: $$

HOURS: Lunch, Wed-Mon, 11AM to 2:30PM
Dinner, Wed-Mon, 5PM to 8:30PM • CLOSED TUESDAY

WHAT TO EXPECT: Dim Sum!! • Very Casual Atmosphere
Great For A Quick Lunch • Lots Of Parking Available

BEST BITES: Steamed Spare Ribs in Black Bean Sauce
Chicken ShuMai • Shanghai Style Dumplings
Honey Glazed BBQ Pork • Crispy Shrimp Toast

SCAN FOR MENU

SOME BASICS

Reservations:	NO
Spirits:	BEER/WINE
Parking:	LOT
Outdoor Dining:	NO

DOGGYSTYLE

1544 Main Street
941-260-5835
hotdogswithstyle.com

DOWNTOWN	AMERICAN	COST: $

HOURS: Mon-Sat, 11AM to 6PM
CLOSED SUNDAY

WHAT TO EXPECT: Hot Dogs, Lots Of Them! • Good For Kids
Quick Lunch Spot • Fast, Friendly Service

BEST BITES: Signature Dogs (Chicago, NY, Detroit, KC, California)
Half Pound Burgers! • Chili Cheese Fries
Handspun Shakes

SCAN FOR MENU

SOME BASICS

Reservations:	NO
Spirits:	BEER
Parking:	STREET
Outdoor Dining:	YES

DOLCE ITALIA

6551 Gateway Avenue
941-921-7007
dolceitaliarestaurant.com

GULF GATE	ITALIAN	COST: $$

HOURS: Mon-Sat, 5PM to 9PM
CLOSED SUNDAY

WHAT TO EXPECT: Great For A Date • Good Wine List
Lots Of Atmosphere • Family Owned

BEST BITES: Burrata • Caprese • Trenne Dolce Italia
Gnocchi Di Patate Al Quatro Formaggi • Lasagna Emiliana
Veal Scallopini • Torte Al Limoncello

SOME BASICS

SCAN FOR MENU

Reservations:	YES
Spirits:	BEER/WINE
Parking:	LOT
Outdoor Dining:	NO

DOUBLE DEEZ CHICAGO STYLE HOT DOGS   **NEW**

3009 Gulf Drive N
941-251-5595
doubledeezami.com

HOLMES BEACH	AMERICAN	COST: $

HOURS: Wed-Sat, 12PM to 8PM • Sun, 12PM to 7PM
CLOSED MONDAY & TUESDAY

WHAT TO EXPECT: It's a "Chicago" Hot Dog Stand! • Family Friendly
Super, super casual • Great For A Quick Lunch On The Go

BEST BITES: Chicago Style Hot Dog • Italian Beef Sandwich
Maxwell Street Polish Sausage • Double Deez Wrigley Combo
Cheesy Beef

SOME BASICS

SCAN FOR MENU

Reservations:	NO
Spirits:	NONE
Parking:	LOT
Outdoor Dining:	YES

DRIFT KITCHEN

700 Benjamin Franklin Drive (Lido Beach Resort)
941-388-2161
lidobeachresort.com/dining/drift

LIDO KEY	**AMERICAN**	**COST: $$**

HOURS: Daily, 7AM to 10PM
Happy Hour Daily, 4PM to 6PM

WHAT TO EXPECT: Upscale Dining • 180° Gulf Views
Lido Beach Resort

BEST BITES: Traditional Eggs Benedict • Cuban Eggs
Crispy Crab Cake • Charcuterie Board • Lido Caesar
Pizza & Flatbreads • Rigatoni Bolognese • Key Lime Pie

SCAN FOR MENU

SOME BASICS

Reservations:	YES
Spirits:	FULL BAR
Parking:	LOT
Outdoor Dining:	NO

DRUNKEN POET CAFÉ

1572 Main Street
941-955-8404
drunkenpoetcafesrq.com

DOWNTOWN	**THAI**	**COST: $$**

HOURS: Sun-Thur, 11AM to 10PM
Fri & Sat, 11AM to 12AM

WHAT TO EXPECT: Casual Atmosphere • Good Vegan Options
Later Night Dining • Great For Small Groups

BEST BITES: Pinky In The Blanket • Crispy Duck Basil
Pad Thai • Pad Kee Mao • Thai Spare Ribs
Duck Noodle Soup • Sushi!! • Fried Ice Cream

SCAN FOR MENU

SOME BASICS

Reservations:	YES
Spirits:	BEER/WINE
Parking:	STREET
Outdoor Dining:	YES

DRY DOCK WATERFRONT RESTAURANT

412 Gulf of Mexico Drive (Marker 6 By Boat)
941-383-0102
drydockwaterfrontgrill.com

LONGBOAT KEY	SEAFOOD	COST: $$

HOURS: Sun-Thur, 11AM to 9PM
Fri & Sat, 11AM to 10PM

WHAT TO EXPECT: Great Water View • Local Seafood • Happy Hour
Good For Groups • Opentable Reservations

BEST BITES: Lobster Bites • Oysters Rockefeller • Fishcamp Chowder
Caesar Salad • Linguine with Clams • Boathouse Tacos
Citrus Grouper • Ribeye Steak • Lobster Rolls

SOME BASICS

SCAN FOR MENU

Reservations:	YES
Spirits:	FULL BAR
Parking:	LOT
Outdoor Dining:	YES

DUTCH VALLEY RESTAURANT

6721 South Tamiami Trail
941-924-1770
dutchvalleyrestaurant.net

SOUTH TRAIL	AMERICAN	COST: $$

HOURS: Daily, 7AM to 9PM

WHAT TO EXPECT: Comfort Food • Casual Dining • Est. 1972!
Good For Kids • Early Dining Crowd

BEST BITES: Daily Specials • Homemade Soups • Eggs Benedict
Omelets • Classic French Dip • Sirloin Bacon Burger
BLT • Broasted Chicken! • Lamb Shank • Meat Loaf

SOME BASICS

SCAN FOR MENU

Reservations:	NO
Spirits:	BEER/WINE
Parking:	LOT
Outdoor Dining:	NO

The Breakfast Company
Homemade Pita Bread

Dimitri Syros

INGREDIENTS
2 cups milk
½ cup honey
½ cup margarine
2 tsp salt
2 packets active dry yeast
½ cup warm water
2 tsp sugar
8 cups all purpose flour
2 eggs

METHOD
Boil milk, then remove to large bowl. Add honey, margarine, and salt to the milk. Stir until margarine is melted. Set aside and cool until lukewarm.

Combine yeast, warm water, and sugar. Stir until sugar is dissolved. Set aside for ten minutes.

Add 4 cups of the flour to the lukewarm milk mixture and beat well. Mix in the egg and the yeast mixture to the flour mix. Add remaining flour slowly until a dough is formed.

Turn out on a floured surface and knead for two minutes. Place dough in an oiled bowl, cover with plastic and store in a warm place.

Punch down and divide into 16 balls. Roll into flat disks.

Heat a large skillet to medium-high heat. Sear on both sides for 1-2 minutes. Enjoy!!

Serves 16

The Breakfast Company is a family-owned breakfast and lunch restaurant specializing in warm customer service and homemade baked goods. The Breakfast Company is known for their award-winning cinnamon rolls and jumbo muffins as well as hand-cut French toast and hearty skillet bowls for breakfast. For lunch, The Breakfast Company returns to its Greek roots serving the best gyro sandwiches in town.

DUVAL'S FRESH. LOCAL. SEAFOOD.
1435 Main Street
941-312-4001
duvalsfreshlocalseafood.com

DOWNTOWN	AMERICAN	COST: $$$

HOURS: Sun-Thur, 11AM to 10PM
Fri & Sat, 11AM to 11PM

WHAT TO EXPECT: Brunch • Opentable Reservations
Great Happy Hour • Free Shuttle To The Restaurant

BEST BITES: Lump Crab Cake • Seafood Bruschetta • Po' Boys!
Duval's BLT • Chicken Cutlet Parmesan • Wedge Salad
Bouillabaisse • Duval's Seafood Sampler • Bread Pudding

SCAN FOR MENU

SOME BASICS
Reservations:	YES
Spirits:	FULL BAR
Parking:	STREET
Outdoor Dining:	YES

EL MELVIN COCINA MEXICANA
1355 Main Street
941-366-1618
elmelvin.com

DOWNTOWN	MEXICAN	COST: $$

HOURS: Sun-Thur, 11AM to 10PM
Fri & Sat, 11AM to 11PM

WHAT TO EXPECT: Casual Mexican Cuisine • Good For Groups
Great Margaritas! • "Mex-Eclectic" • Weekend Brunch

BEST BITES: Fajitas • Queso Fundido • Agua Chile
Enchilada Divorciadas • Combo Platters
Short Rib Birria Chimichanga • Tres Leches

SCAN FOR MENU

SOME BASICS
Reservations:	YES
Spirits:	FULL BAR
Parking:	STREET
Outdoor Dining:	YES

EL TORO BRAVO
3218 Clark Road
941-924-0006
eltorobravosarasota.com

MEXICAN	COST: $$

HOURS: Tue-Thur, 11AM to 8PM • Fri, 11AM to 9PM
Sat, 5PM to 9PM • CLOSED SUNDAY & MONDAY

WHAT TO EXPECT: Great for families • Super casual dining
Usually busy • Online reservations • Lots of parking

BEST BITES: Jalapeños Rellenos • Queso Blanco
Shrimp Chimichanga • Combination Plates
Chips & Homemade Salsa • Deep Fried Cheesecake

SCAN FOR MENU

SOME BASICS
Reservations:	YES
Spirits:	BEER/WINE
Parking:	LOT
Outdoor Dining:	NO

EUPHEMIA HAYE

5540 Gulf of Mexico Drive
941-383-3633
euphemiahaye.com

LONGBOAT KEY	AMERICAN	COST: $$$$

HOURS: Tue-Thur, 5:30PM to 9PM • Fri & Sat, 5PM to 9:30PM
Sun, 5:30PM to 9PM • CLOSED MONDAY

WHAT TO EXPECT: Great For A Date • The Haye Loft For Dessert!
Fine Dining Experience • Great For Special Occasions

BEST BITES: Snails Leslie • Classic Caesar Salad
Tagliatelle Alla Carbonara • Roasted Duckling
Euphemia's Prime Peppered Steak • Key West Snapper

SOME BASICS

SCAN FOR MENU

Reservations:	YES
Spirits:	FULL BAR
Parking:	LOT
Outdoor Dining·	NO

1592 WOOD FIRED KITCHEN & COCKTAILS

1592 Main Street
941-365-2234
1592srq.com

DOWNTOWN	GREEK	COST: $$

HOURS: Mon-Thur, 11AM to 10PM • Fri & Sat, 11AM to 11PM
Sun, 4PM to 10PM

WHAT TO EXPECT: Great Casual Dining • Great Happy Hour
Nice Street-Side Dining • Good Downtown Lunch Spot

BEST BITES: Farmers Market Hummus • Saganaki
Spicy Feta Spread • Pulled Lamb Open Faced Pita
Moussaka • Montreal's "Poutine" • Pizza!

SOME BASICS

SCAN FOR MENU

Reservations:	YES
Spirits:	BEER/WINE
Parking:	STREET
Outdoor Dining:	YES

481 GOURMET
481 North Orange Avenue
941-362-0400
481gourmetsarasota.com

ROSEMARY DIST	AMERICAN	COST: $$$

HOURS: Wed-Sun, 4PM to 9:30PM • Sunday Brunch, 11AM to 3PM
CLOSED MONDAY & TUESDAY

WHAT TO EXPECT: Great Outdoor Dining Space • Seasonal Menu
Sunday Brunch • Upscale Atmosphere

BEST BITES: Watermelon Basil Salad • 481 Meatball
Italian Pomodoro • Bouillabaisse • Seared Scallops
Osso Bucco Braised Short Rib • Poached Pear

SCAN FOR MENU

SOME BASICS

Reservations:	YES
Spirits:	FULL BAR
Parking:	STREET
Outdoor Dining:	YES

F.L.A. DELI
NEW

2805 Proctor Road
941-217-5710
szakali.com/home

	EUROPEAN	COST: $$

HOURS: Tues, 1PM to 6PM • Wed-Fri, 11AM to 6PM
Sat, 11AM to 4PM • CLOSED SUNDAY & MONDAY

WHAT TO EXPECT: The Former M&M European Deli • Market
Hungarian Cuisine • Great For a To-Go

BEST BITES: Polish Breakfast Sandwich • Gyro Lamb/Chicken
Ukrainian Borscht Soup • Hungarian Fisher Soup
Hunter Stew • Homemade Pierogi • Dobos Cake

SCAN FOR MENU

SOME BASICS

Reservations:	NO
Spirits:	BEER/WINE
Parking:	LOT
Outdoor Dining:	NO

FAICCO'S ITALIAN HEROS AND GRILL

3590 Webber Street
941-960-1395
faiccossarasota.com

	DELI	COST: $$

HOURS: Sat-Thur, 10:30AM to 6PM • Fri, 10:30AM to 7PM
CLOSED SUNDAY

WHAT TO EXPECT: Good For Families • Perfect For A Quick Lunch
Family Owned & Operated • Super Casual

BEST BITES: Sausage Rolls • Spicy Italian Hero
Muffuletta • Roast Beef Italiano • Chicken Broccoli Rabe
Homemade Porchetta • Grilled Hot Dogs

SOME BASICS

SCAN FOR MENU

Reservations:	NO
Spirits:	NONE
Parking:	LOT
Outdoor Dining:	YES

FAT POINT BREWING

NEW

257 North Cattlemen Road
941-491-2827
fatpoint.com

UTC	AMERICAN	COST: $$

HOURS: Mon-Thur, 12PM to 9PM • Fri & Sat, 12PM to 10PM
Sun, 12PM to 8PM

WHAT TO EXPECT: Locally Brewed Beer • Open Mic Night
4 Packs To Go • Casual Brewery Atmosphere

BEST BITES: Gator Bites • Smoked Fish Dip • Shrimp Po' Boy
Umami Burger • Cobb Salad • Coastal Salad
Honey Garlic Shrimp

SOME BASICS

SCAN FOR MENU

Reservations:	NO
Spirits:	BEER/WINE
Parking:	LOT
Outdoor Dining:	NO

FIGARO BISTRO

1944 Hillview Street
941-960-2109
figaro-bistro.com

SOUTHSIDE VILLAGE	FRENCH	COST: $$$

HOURS: Tue-Thur, 5PM to 9PM
Fri & Sat, 5PM to 9:30PM CLOSED SUNDAY & MONDAY

WHAT TO EXPECT: Authentic, Upscale French Cuisine
Nice Wine List • Try The Escargots De Bourgogne

BEST BITES: Escargots Meurette • Salade Lyonnaise
Moules Frites • Boeuf Bourguignon • Filet de Bœuf
Cassoulet Toulousain • Crêpe Suzette

SCAN FOR MENU

SOME BASICS

Reservations:	YES
Spirits:	BEER/WINE
Parking:	STREET
Outdoor Dining:	YES

FINS AT SHARKY'S

1600 Harbor Drive South
941-999-3467
finsatsharkys.com

VENICE	AMERICAN	COST: $$$

HOURS: Lunch, Daily, 11:45PM to 2:30PM
Dinner, Daily, 4PM to 10PM

WHAT TO EXPECT: Beachfront Dining • "Fins Frenzy" Happy Hour
Good Wine List • "Steakhouse With A Serious Seafood Side"

BEST BITES: Cheese & Charcuterie Plate • Josper Grilled Octopus
Lobster Potato Nachos • Heirloom Tomato Caprese
Smoked Rib Eye • Faroe Island Salmon

SCAN FOR MENU

SOME BASICS

Reservations:	YES
Spirits:	FULL BAR
Parking:	LOT
Outdoor Dining:	YES

FLAVIO'S ON MAIN

1766 Main Street
941-960-2305
flaviosonmain.com

DOWNTOWN	ITALIAN	COST: $$$

HOURS: Mon-Thur, 4PM to 9PM • Fri & Sat, 4PM to 9:30PM
CLOSED SUNDAY

WHAT TO EXPECT: Daily Happy Hour • Classic Italian Cuisine
Upscale, Comfortable Atmosphere • Good Wine List

BEST BITES: Fritto Misto • Tuna Tartare • Linguine Carbonara
Agnolotti ai Funghi • Branzino • Veal Osso Buco
Pollo al Milanese

SOME BASICS

SCAN FOR MENU

Reservations:	YES
Spirits:	FULL BAR
Parking:	STREET
Outdoor Dining:	YES

FLAVIO'S ON SIESTA

5239 Ocean Boulevard
941-349-0995
flaviosbrickovenandbar.com

SIESTA KEY	ITALIAN	COST: $$$

HOURS: Daily, 4PM to 10PM
Happy Hour, 4PM to 6PM

WHAT TO EXPECT: Homemade Italian Cuisine • Brick Oven Pizza
Good Meet-Up Spot • Siesta Village Location

BEST BITES: Brick Oven Pizza! • Mozzarella in Carrozza
Spiedino Di Gamberi • Burrata e Prosciutto
Insalata Cesare • Pappardelle Ai Porcini • Nodino Di Vitello

SOME BASICS

SCAN FOR MENU

Reservations:	YES
Spirits:	FULL BAR
Parking:	LOT
Outdoor Dining:	YES

FLORENCE AND THE SPICE BOYS

4990 South Tamiami Trail
941-405-3890

THE LANDINGS	MIDDLE EASTERN	COST: $$

HOURS: Mon-Sat, 11AM to 8PM
CLOSED SUNDAY

WHAT TO EXPECT: Israeli-Influenced Cuisine • Vegan/Veg Options
Nice Outdoor Dining Space • Convenient Online Ordering

BEST BITES: Chicken Shawarma Salad! • Hummus Sweet Corn
Harissa Shrimp Skewer • Corn Ribs • Bhel Puri
Mushroom Pita • Spice Boys Organic Date "Snickers"

SCAN FOR MENU

SOME BASICS

Reservations:	NO
Spirits:	NONE
Parking:	LOT
Outdoor Dining:	YES

FOOD + BEER

6528 Superior Avenue*
941-952-3361
eatfooddrinkbeer.com

GULF GATE	AMERICAN	COST: $$

HOURS: Mon-Thur, 11AM to 1AM • Fri, 11AM to 2AM
Sat, 10AM to 2AM • Sun, 10AM to 1AM

WHAT TO EXPECT: Super Casual • Good Local Beer Selection
Later Night Menu • Sat. & Sun. Brunch

BEST BITES: Down The Hatch Burger • Malibu Barbie Wrap
Birria Tacos • Cali Hot Cobb Bowl • Fried Goat Cheese
Buffalo Chicken Wedge • Red Velvet Oreos

SCAN FOR MENU

SOME BASICS

Reservations:	NO
Spirits:	BEER/WINE
Parking:	STREET/LOT
Outdoor Dining:	NO

FORK & HEN

2801 North Tamiami Trail
941-960-1212
forkandhenssrq.com

NORTH TRAIL	AMERICAN	COST: $$

HOURS: Tues-Thur, 11:30AM to 7:30PM • Fri-Sun, 11:30AM to 8PM
CLOSED MONDAY

WHAT TO EXPECT: Chef-Driven Menu • Super Casual Dining
Scratch Kitchen • Ringling School Neighborhood

BEST BITES: Creole Brussels & Cauliflower • Chicken Parm
El Chido Hot Chicken Sandwich • The Hitman Burger
Watermelon & Feta Salad • Chicken & Waffles

SOME BASICS

SCAN FOR MENU

Reservations:	NO
Spirits:	NONE
Parking:	LOT
Outdoor Dining:	YES

GECKO'S GRILL & PUB

6606 South Tamiami Trail*
941-248-2020
geckosgrill.com

SOUTH TRAIL	AMERICAN	COST: $$

HOURS: Daily, 11AM to 10PM

WHAT TO EXPECT: Great To Watch A Game • Yelp Waitlist
Good Burgers • "American Pub Food"

BEST BITES: Blue Cheese Chips • Loaded Potato Scoops
Wings! • Black Beans & Rice • The Ultimate Cobb
Flatbreads • Wraps • Burgers • Cuban Sub

SOME BASICS

SCAN FOR MENU

Reservations:	NO
Spirits:	FULL BAR
Parking:	LOT
Outdoor Dining:	YES

Living in a Vegan Paradise

By Kaye Warr

Welcome to Sarasota, where sun-kissed beaches meet a diverse culinary scene that caters brilliantly to plant-based palates whilst also satisfying passionate carnivores and vociferous pescatarians.

I've embarked on a culinary adventure of my own lately, courtesy of my newfound romance with a fantastic guy who just happens to be vegan.

As someone deeply entrenched in the world of food writing, as well as being a self-proclaimed "woman about town," I've taken it upon myself to uncover all the local vegan hotspots and hidden gems in our charming city-by-the-sea. Now, while I can appreciate a good steak as much as the next Yellowstone enthusiast, this journey has revealed two surprising outcomes:

Firstly, I've fallen for the way that eating vegan (and dating a vegan) makes me feel, and secondly, Sarasota is currently dishing out some of the most extraordinary plant-based cuisine I've ever had the pleasure of tasting—yes, even surpassing experiences in vegan meccas like Los Angeles, Chicago, and Manhattan.

Sarasota's dining landscape is embracing the vegan wave with open arms. From quirky cafes to upscale joints, this guide is your key to navigating through the best plant-based spots.

Sarasota's restaurants have not just caught on to this trend but have passionately curated menus that highlight the bounty of locally sourced, plant-powered goodness.

Get ready for a culinary journey through the city's diverse offerings, where each spot isn't only about cruelty-free dining but is a genuine celebration of flavors. Whether you're a seasoned vegan or just dipping your toes into the plant-based world, whether it's early morning or late night – we've got you covered.

BREAKFAST

Full on Vegan: Project Coffee

It took me three visits to realize that everything on this menu is plant-based: I can be forgiven for my ignorance because nothing on this menu "tastes" vegan. The baked goods are a symphony of flaky, buttery, crunchy, and heavenly. The biscuits are Southern grandma-level good. And mark my words, the two-handed breakfast sandwich is a potential game-changer – it might just turn your significant other vegan if that's a path you're inclined to explore.

Vegan Curious: Perq

Most of the cool coffee shops currently anchoring the city of Sarasota can trace their roots back to this one – Keith and Erin Zolner having been making coffee hip for over a decade, and they trained many of the baristas and shop owners at your favorite places. These days, the staff at Perq consists of Keith making the coffee and Erin making the ridiculously tasty food. Keto? No problem. Gluten-Free? She's got you. Vegan? Open wide, here comes the delectable, instagrammable, vegan toast – thank me later.

LUNCH

Full on Vegan: Fam Kitchen

Question: What could be better than a 100% vegan food truck parked in a sunny courtyard littered with colorful picnic tables just a couple of blocks from Sarasota Bay? Answer: Nothing.

I'm here to tell you that Sarasota's best Reuben Sandwich, piled high with real pastrami, can be found at Palm Avenue Deli. But Sarasota's best plant-based Grilled Reuben, piled high with tempeh, is served at Fam Kitchen and is so good that I've yet to try any of the other handhelds – even though my boyfriend swears by the Forever Summer BLT.

Raw Vegan: Ionie

One of the best things that happened to me this year is that Ionie opened a beautiful new sit-down restaurant right next to Whole Foods in downtown Sarasota. If you haven't yet visited this raw vegan oasis, what are you waiting for? Order my favorite sandwich, "The Martin," and wash it down with a beautiful cold-pressed juice. Pressed for time? Peruse the raw vegan grab-and-go case. If you see "The Shake" Smoothie in the case, then that's your sign that you've beaten me to it, and to the victor go the spoils.

Vegan Curious: Boo's

Boo's Dog Bar is man's best friend's favorite place to go. Finally, a place that not only welcomes your dog but encourages you to bring your dog allows your dog to play with other dogs, and serves your dog meals specifically designed with your dog in mind. Boo's offers a vegan menu that includes vegan versions of Chef Dave Grammar's perfect wood-fired pizzas. All dogs go to heaven, all vegans with dogs go to Boo's.

DINNER

Full on Vegan: Ka Papa

Ka Papa is a stunningly beautiful upscale dining experience in the charming neighborhood of Southside Village. Go for the Escargots, the Charcuterie Board, the Warm Brie, and the Lemon Alfredo Pasta; stay for the fact that every single one of these dishes (and all the others, too) are vegan and delicious. Leave room for dessert - get both sorbets and get them with the whipped "cream." Oh, Ka Papa!

Vegan Curious: Lucile Pizza & Wine Bar
I've said it before, and I'll say it again: Lucile is a sexy place.

Take a date. Share the pizza. Share a bottle of wine. Share the tiramisu. Believe it or not, not all wine is vegan. Lucile has vegan wine. The pizza can also be vegan. But forget what I said earlier: don't share the vegan tiramisu. I don't care how much you think you like your date – you'll want your own tiramisu.

Late Night Vegan: Tamiami Tap

You know what you don't get a lot of when you're vegan? Bar food and late-night snacks. Tamiami Tap has some of the tastiest vegan bar food in town; they serve it late, and, more often than not, they serve it with live music in the open-air courtyard. Vegan Chili Nachos for the win!

Kaye Warr hails from Johannesburg, South Africa, where her passionate and boisterous family engendered a love of food and socializing at an impressionable age. Kaye began her career as a freelance epicurean adventurer under the guise of "The Dining Diva." Kaye feels especially privileged to write for a beautiful publication with local integrity such as Edible Sarasota.

GENTILE BROTHERS CHEESESTEAKS
7523 South Tamiami Trail
941-926-0441
gentilesteaks.com

SOUTH TRAIL	AMERICAN	COST: $

HOURS: Mon-Sat, 11AM to 7PM
CLOSED SUNDAY

WHAT TO EXPECT: Philly Experience • No Frills Dining
Easy On The Wallet • Family Owned • Good For Kids

BEST BITES: Clemenza Cheesesteak Sandwich • Italian Hoagie
South Philly Sandwich • Cheese Fries

SOME BASICS

SCAN FOR MENU

Reservations:	NO
Spirits:	NONE
Parking:	LOT
Outdoor Dining:	NO

GOOD LIQUID BREWING

1570 Lakefront Drive
941-238-6466
goodliquidbrewingcompany.com

WATERSIDE PLACE	BREW PUB	COST: $$

HOURS: Sun-Thur, 11AM to 9PM
Fri & Sat, 11AM to 10PM

WHAT TO EXPECT: Brew Pub • Fantastic Outdoor Gathering Area
Busy On Weekends

BEST BITES: GLB Pretzel • Shrimp & Crab Cakes
BBQ Chicken Salad • The Hay Stack Burger
GL Double Stack Burger • Wood Grilled "Brewzettas"

SCAN FOR MENU

SOME BASICS
Reservations:	NO
Spirits:	FULL BAR
Parking:	STREET
Outdoor Dining:	YES

GRANDPA'S SCHNITZEL

2700 Stickney Point Road
941-922-3888
grandpas-schnitzel.com

	GERMAN	COST: $$

HOURS: Mon-Sat, 8AM to 1:30PM • Mon-Sat, 5PM to 9PM
CLOSED SUNDAY

WHAT TO EXPECT: Real German Cuisine • Family Owned
Schnitzels! • Lots Of Parking

BEST BITES: "Schnitzel-Burgers" • Currywurst • Schweinbraten
Bratwurst • German Apple Strudel • Pfannkuchen

SCAN FOR MENU

SOME BASICS
Reservations:	YES
Spirits:	BEER/WINE
Parking:	LOT
Outdoor Dining:	NO

BURGER TIME!
SOME OF SARASOTA'S BEST

The Cottage • 153 Avenida Messina • 312-9300
WHAT TO EXPECT: Upscale casual on Siesta Key. The Billionaire Burger will not disappoint. Grab a cold craft beer to drink!

Hob Nob Drive-In • 1701 N. Washington Blvd. • 955-5001
WHAT TO EXPECT: Always one of Sarasota's best burger stops. Old school, nothing fancy. The "Hob Nob" burger basket is a must.

Indigenous • 239 S. Links Ave. • 706-4740
WHAT TO EXPECT: This one is always a pleasant surprise. Chef Phelps puts out a delicious burger. Can you say, bacon jam?

Island House Tap & Grill • 5110 Ocean Blvd. • 487-8116
WHAT TO EXPECT: They have a super secret prep method that turns out a perfectly cooked, juicy, and delicious burger every time!

Made • 1990 Main St. • 953-2900
WHAT TO EXPECT: Niman Ranch beef + billionaire bacon. What more do you really need to say? Delicious! Great sides, too.

Mouthole Smashburgers • 4571 Clark Rd. • 544-1361
WHAT TO EXPECT: If you like a smash-style burger then this is your spot. Simple, delicious burgers. Locals love these!

Patrick's 1481 • 1481 Main St. • 955-1481
WHAT TO EXPECT: It's all about the burger at Patrick's. This restaurant is a downtown institution. Try it and you'll know why.

Shakespeare's • 3550 S. Osprey Ave. • 364-5938
WHAT TO EXPECT: A caramelized onion & Brie burger! English pub atmosphere. Lots and lots of craft beer to wash it all down.

Read Our Yearlong Burger Series
A BURGER A WEEK!

THE GRASSHOPPER

7253 South Tamiami Trail
941-923-3688
thegrasshoppertexmex.com

SOUTH TRAIL	MEXICAN	COST: $$

HOURS: Mon-Sat, 11AM to 10PM
Happy Hour, 3:30PM to 5:30PM

WHAT TO EXPECT: Easy On The Wallet • Happy Hour
Good Cocktail Selection • Good For Groups

BEST BITES: Huevos Rancheros • Signature Queso • Guacamole
Combination Plate • Taco Plate • Tamale Plate
Veggie Chili Rellenos • Menudo

SCAN FOR MENU

SOME BASICS

Reservations:	YES
Spirits:	FULL BAR
Parking:	LOT
Outdoor Dining:	NO

GRAZE STREET AMI

3218 E. Bay Drive
941-896-6320
grazestreetami.com

HOLMES BEACH	AMERICAN	COST: $

HOURS: Wed-Fri, 11AM to 6PM • Sat, 10AM to 6PM
Sun, 10AM to 3PM • CLOSED MONDAY & TUESDAY

WHAT TO EXPECT: Bakery & Gourmet Shop • Super Casual
Limited Sandwich Menu

BEST BITES: Caprese Sandwich • Green Goddess Sandwich
Beachy BLT • Tuna Salad • Cookies Every Day!

SCAN FOR MENU

SOME BASICS

Reservations:	NO
Spirits:	NONE
Parking:	STREET
Outdoor Dining:	NO

GROVE

10670 Boardwalk Loop
941-893-4321
grovelwr.com

LAKEWOOD RANCH	AMERICAN	COST: $$$

HOURS: Mon-Thur, 11:30AM to 10PM • Fri, 11:30AM to 10:30PM
Sat, 10AM to 10:30PM • Sun, 10AM to 10PM

WHAT TO EXPECT: Happy Hour • Culinary Cocktails
Weekend Brunch 10AM to 3PM • Wine Dinners

BEST BITES: Mussels & Blue • Thai Cauliflower • Tuna Nachos
Flatbreads • NE Clam Chowder • Baby Wedge Salad
Jambalaya • Sushi • Grouper Oscar • Pork Osso Bucco

SCAN FOR MENU

SOME BASICS

Reservations:	YES
Spirits:	FULL BAR
Parking:	LOT
Outdoor Dining:	YES

HARRY'S CONTINENTAL KITCHENS

525 St. Judes Drive
941-383-0777
harryskitchen.com

LONGBOAT KEY	AMERICAN	COST: $$$

HOURS: Restaurant - Daily, 9AM to 9PM
Deli - 11AM to 7PM

WHAT TO EXPECT: Great For A Date • Monthly Wine Events
Upscale Florida Dining • Visit The "Corner Store"

BEST BITES: Shrimp-Cargot • Harry's Famous Crab Cakes
Fresh Chunky Gazpacho • Sautéed Veal Medallions
Roast Maple Leaf Half Duckling • Peanut Butter Pie

SCAN FOR MENU

SOME BASICS

Reservations:	YES
Spirits:	FULL BAR
Parking:	LOT
Outdoor Dining:	YES

VEGETARIAN OR VEGAN?
HERE ARE SARASOTA'S BEST PLACES

Vegetarian and vegan lifestyles both offer a healthy way of eating. But, as any one who keeps either of these diets knows, dining out can sometimes be more than a challenge. I mean, how many grilled cheese sandwiches can one person consume? Don't despair. We're here to help. Sarasota has its share of options for those who choose a meat-free existence. Keep in mind that the places listed below may not be strictly vegan/veg only. But, they will offer some nice menu options.

Florence and the Spice Boys • 4990 S. Tamiami Trl. • 405-3890
THE HIGHLIGHTS: Hummus, Baba Ganoush, Falafel and lots more. Lots of variety here. Try a Rainbow Bowl!

Ka Papa Cuisine • 1830 S. Osprey Ave. • 600-8590
THE HIGHLIGHTS: Sarasota's only 100% plant-based and vegan full service restaurant. Excellent menu of large and small plates.

Lila • 1576 Main St. • 296-1042
THE HIGHLIGHTS: Named one of the best vegetarian restaurants in the country by OpenTable. Refined vegetarian cuisine.

Organic Farmer's Table • 6538 Gateway Ave. • 362-3276
THE HIGHLIGHTS: Great for vegan/veg and those that are not. The Beet Carpaccio is great. Or try a Vegan Fiesta!

Spice Station • 14 N. Lemon Ave. • 343-2894
THE HIGHLIGHTS: Fantastic Thai cuisine. They've got a large section of vegetarian dishes on their menu. Cozy dining space.

Tandoor • 8447 Cooper Creek Blvd • 926-3077
THE HIGHLIGHTS: Indian cuisine lends itself to a vegetarian diet. There are vegetarian variations on most dishes. Since 2001.

HOB NOB DRIVE-IN RESTAURANT
1701 North Washington Boulevard (301 & 17th St.)
941-955-5001
hobnobdrivein.com

DOWNTOWN	AMERICAN	COST: $

HOURS: Mon-Sat, 7AM to 8PM
Sun, 8AM to 4PM

WHAT TO EXPECT: Easy On The Wallet • Fun! • Great For Kids
Sarasota's Oldest Drive-In. • Great Burger!

BEST BITES: Hob Nob Burger • Patty Melt • Chili Cheese Dog
Grilled Ham & Cheese • Tuna Melt • Fried Mushrooms
Onion Rings • Ice Cream Floats!

SOME BASICS
Reservations: NO
Spirits: BEER/WINE
Parking: LOT
Outdoor Dining: YES

SCAN FOR MENU

THE HUB BAJA GRILL
5148 Ocean Boulevard
941-349-6800
thehubsiestakey.com

SIESTA KEY	AMERICAN	COST: $$

HOURS: Sun-Thur, 11AM to 10PM • Fri & Sat, 11AM to 11PM

WHAT TO EXPECT: Island Dining Experience • Good For Families
Busy In Season • Live Music Daily • Happy Hour Specials

BEST BITES: The Hub Margarita • Lobster Bisque • Baja Salad
Grande Nachos • Mahi Lettuce Wrap • The Hub Cuban
Short Rib Taco Sofrito • Baby Back Ribs

SOME BASICS
Reservations: NO
Spirits: FULL BAR
Parking: STREET
Outdoor Dining: YES

SCAN FOR MENU

IL PANIFICIO

1703 Main Street*
941-921-5570
panificiousa.com

DOWNTOWN	ITALIAN	COST: $$

HOURS: Daily, 10AM to 9PM

WHAT TO EXPECT: Great For Lunch • Easy On The Wallet
Family Friendly• Nice Spot For A Lunch Meet-Up

BEST BITES: Eggplant Rollatini • Italian Salad • Prosciutto Sub
Meatball Parm Sandwich • Pizza By The Slice
Stromboli • Sausage, Pepper & Onion Sandwich

SCAN FOR MENU

SOME BASICS
Reservations:	NO
Spirits:	BEER/WINE
Parking:	STREET
Outdoor Dining:	YES

INDIGENOUS RESTAURANT

239 South Links Avenue
941-706-4740
indigenoussarasota.com

TOWLES CT	AMERICAN	COST: $$$

HOURS: Tues-Sat, 5:30PM to 8:30PM
CLOSED SUNDAY & MONDAY

WHAT TO EXPECT: Great For A Date • Fine Dining, Casual Feel
Towles Court Neighborhood • Limited Outdoor Seating

BEST BITES: Wild Mushroom Bisque • Red Curry Fish Dip
Cobia Crudo • Pork Funchi • My Uncle's Burger
Everglades Baked Shrimp & Scallops • Buttermilk Pie

SCAN FOR MENU

SOME BASICS
Reservations:	YES
Spirits:	BEER/WINE
Parking:	LOT/STREET
Outdoor Dining:	YES

ISLAND HOUSE TAP & GRILL

5110 Ocean Boulevard
941-487-8116
islandhousetapandgrill.com

SIESTA KEY	AMERICAN	COST: $$

HOURS: Daily, 11AM to 10PM

WHAT TO EXPECT: Great Craft Beers • Fantastic Burgers & Tacos
Outdoor Patio • Local Favorite • Daily Specials

BEST BITES: Duck Fat Fries • Chicken Lollipops • Guac n' Chips
Endless Summer Salad • Carnitas Bowl
Carne Asada Tacos • Steakhouse Burger

SOME BASICS

SCAN FOR MENU

Reservations:	NO
Spirits:	BEER/WINE
Parking:	LOT
Outdoor Dining:	YES

JACK DUSTY

1111 Ritz-Carlton Drive
941-309-2266
ritzcarlton.com/en/hotels/florida/sarasota/dining/jack-dusty

DOWNTOWN	SEAFOOD	COST: $$$

HOURS: Breakfast, lunch, and dinner daily

WHAT TO EXPECT: Walking Distance To Downtown • Water View
Handmade Cocktails • Opentable Reservations

BEST BITES: Smoked Fish Dip • Sarasota Cioppino • Lobster Roll
Jack's Fish Tacos • South Crispy Half Chicken
Panzenella Salad • Roasted Grouper

SOME BASICS

SCAN FOR MENU

Reservations:	YES
Spirits:	FULL BAR
Parking:	VALET
Outdoor Dining:	YES

JERSEY GIRL BAGELS

5275 University Parkway
941-388-8910
jerseygirlbagels.net

UNIVERSITY PARK	DELI	COST: $$

HOURS: Wed-Sun, 7AM to 2PM
CLOSED MONDAY & TUESDAY

WHAT TO EXPECT: NY Style Bagels • Buy One Or A Dozen!
Super Casual • Lots Of Parking • Good For A Carryout

BEST BITES: Egg Salad Sandwich • Lox & Bagel Sandwich
Black & White Cookies • Breakfast Sandwiches

SCAN FOR MENU

SOME BASICS

Reservations:	NO
Spirits:	NONE
Parking:	LOT
Outdoor Dining:	NO

JOEY D'S CHICAGO STYLE EATERY

3811 Kenny Drive*
941-378-8900
joeydsfl.com

	AMERICAN	COST: $$

HOURS: Daily, 11AM to 10PM

WHAT TO EXPECT: Chicago Style Food • Family Friendly
Multiple Locations • Super Casual

BEST BITES: World Famous Chicago Pizza • Stromboli
The Shroom Burger • Original "Chicago Style" Hot Dog
Grilled Maxwell Street Polish • Italian Beef

SCAN FOR MENU

SOME BASICS

Reservations:	NO
Spirits:	BEER/WINE
Parking:	LOT
Outdoor Dining:	YES

JPAN RESTAURANT & SUSHI BAR

3800 South Tamiami Trail (Shops at Siesta Row)*
941-954-5726
jpanrestaurant.com

SHOPS AT SIESTA ROW	JAPANESE	COST: $$

HOURS: Lunch, Mon-Fri, 11:30AM to 2PM
Mon-Sat, 5PM to 9:30PM • Sun, 5PM to 9PM

WHAT TO EXPECT: Great For A Date • Big Sushi Menu
Great Lunch Combos • Opentable Reservations

BEST BITES: Sushi • Sashimi • Bento Boxes • Pork Dumplings
Kfc (Korean Fried Chicken) • Hamachi Chilli
Ramen • Volcano Chicken

SOME BASICS

SCAN FOR MENU

Reservations:	YES
Spirits:	BEER/WINE
Parking:	LOT
Outdoor Dining:	YES

2024 SARASOTA FOOD EVENTS

FORKS & CORKS

WHEN: January 25-29
WHAT: Sponsored by the Sarasota-Manatee Originals. Super
popular food event! Wine dinners, seminars, AND the Grand
Tasting. A must for Sarasota foodies. Tickets go very fast.
INFO: eatlikealocal.com/forksandcorks

FLORIDA WINEFEST & AUCTION

WHEN: March 16
WHAT: This charity event has been providing needed help to
local children's programs for over 30 years. The Charity Brunch &
Auction is a fantastic event! INFO: floridawinefest.org

SAVOR SARASOTA RESTAURANT WEEK

WHEN: June 1-14th
WHAT: This restaurant week spans TWO full weeks. It features
lots of popular restaurants and showcases three course menus.
INFO: savorsarasota.com

JR'S OLD PACKINGHOUSE CAFE

987 South Packinghouse Drive
941-371-9358
packinghousecafe.com

AMERICAN	**COST: $$**

HOURS: Mon-Thur, 11AM to 9PM • Fri & Sat, 11AM to 10PM
CLOSED SUNDAY

WHAT TO EXPECT: Fun For A Date • Live Music
Great Burgers & Cuban Sandwiches

BEST BITES: Queso Burger • Cuban Sandwich OPC Style
Mediterranean Salad • Ropa Vieja • OPC Shrimp
Country Fried Chicken • Key Lime Pie

SCAN FOR MENU

SOME BASICS

Reservations:	NO
Spirits:	FULL BAR
Parking:	LOT
Outdoor Dining:	YES

KA PAPA CUISINE

1830 South Osprey Avenue
941-600-8590
kapapacuisine.com

SOUTHSIDE VILLAGE	**VEGAN**	**COST: $$$**

HOURS: Wed-Sun, 5PM to 9PM

WHAT TO EXPECT: 100% Plant Based Cuisine • Vegan
Casual "Urban" Feel • Southside Village Location

BEST BITES: Spicy Edamame • Baked "Feta" • Grilled "Caesar" Salad
Plum-Miso Glazed Eggplant • Pan Roasted Mushrooms
House-Made Pasta With Walnut Pesto

SCAN FOR MENU

SOME BASICS

Reservations:	YES
Spirits:	BEER/WINE
Parking:	LOT/STREET
Outdoor Dining:	YES

KIYOSHI SUSHI

6550 Gateway Avenue
941-924-3781

GULF GATE	SUSHI	COST: $$

HOURS: Tues-Sat, 5:30PM to 9PM
CLOSED SUNDAY & MONDAY

WHAT TO EXPECT: Traditional Sushi • Casual & Comfortable
Beautiful Presentations

BEST BITES: Maki Rolls • Chicken Katsu • Sashimi Combo
Chirashi Bowl • Hot & Cold Sake • Green Tea Ice Cream

SCAN FOR MENU

SOME BASICS

Reservations:	YES
Spirits:	BEER/WINE
Parking:	STREET/LOT
Outdoor Dining:	NO

KNICK'S TAVERN & GRILL

1818 South Osprey Avenue
941-955-7761
knickstavernandgrill.com

SOUTHSIDE VILLAGE	AMERICAN	COST: $$

HOURS: Mon-Thur, 11:30AM to 9PM • Fri, 11:30AM to 10PM
Sat, 5PM to 10PM • CLOSED SUNDAY

WHAT TO EXPECT: Casual Dining • Busy In Season • Family Owned
Local Favorite • Great Burgers • Daily Specials

BEST BITES: The Ultimate Wedge • Blackened Calamari
Chipotle Crumbled Bleu Cheese Burger • Mussels
Knickole's Chicken Sandwich • Dessert Specials

SCAN FOR MENU

SOME BASICS

Reservations:	YES
Spirits:	BEER/WINE
Parking:	STREET
Outdoor Dining:	YES

SARASOTA MARKETS AND SPECIALTY STORES

A Taste of Europe • 2130 Gulf Gate Dr. • 921-9084
WHAT YOU CAN FIND THERE: Foods from twenty different European countries. Fresh deli, specialty cheeses, beer, wine, and more.

Alpine Steakhouse • 4520 S. Tamiami Trl. • 922-3797
WHAT YOU CAN FIND THERE: Meat market. Skilled butchers, super helpful. Famous for Turducken. Also, full service restaurant.

Artisan Cheese Company • 550 Central Ave. • 951-7860
WHAT YOU CAN FIND THERE: Cheese store. Hard to find small domestic dairies. Lunch menu. Classes. Knowledgeable staff.

Big Water Fish Market • 6641 Midnight Pass Rd. • 554-8101
WHAT YOU CAN FIND THERE: Fresh Florida fish. Great prepared seafood items. Just south of Siesta Key's south bridge.

The Butcher's Block • 3242 17th St. • 955-2822
WHAT YOU CAN FIND THERE: Meat market/butcher shop. Custom cuts, prime meats. Good wine selection. They have gift baskets.

Butcher's Mark • 8519 Cooper Creek Blvd. • 358-6328
WHAT YOU CAN FIND THERE: Sustainable beef. Lots of marinades and pre-marinaded meat. Charcuterie and antipasto.

F.L.A. DELI • 2805 Proctor Rd. • 217-5710
WHAT YOU CAN FIND THERE: European deli and market specializing in Hungarian specialties. Take home some homemade Pierogis!

Geier's Sausage Kitchen • 7447 S. Tamiami Trl. • 923-3004
WHAT YOU CAN FIND THERE: Sausage & more sausage. Sarasota's best German market. Lots of smoked meats and deli items.

Morton's Gourmet Market • 1924 S. Osprey Ave. • 955-9856
WHAT YOU CAN FIND THERE: Upscale gourmet food items including a large selection of cheeses and wine. Great deli & carryout.

SARASOTA MARKETS AND SPECIALTY STORES

Morton's Siesta Market • 205 Canal Rd. • 349-1474
WHAT YOU CAN FIND THERE: Everyday grocery items plus a good selection of prepared foods for lunch and dinner. Cold beer.

Piccolo Italian Market • 6518 Gateway Ave. • 923-2202
WHAT YOU CAN FIND THERE: Italian market. Pastas, sauces, homebaked bread, and homemade Italian sausage. Sandwiches.

Southern Steer Butcher • 4084 Bee Ridge Rd. • 706-2625
WHAT YOU CAN FIND THERE: Big selection of pre-brined beef and chicken. Full butcher shop and lots of specialty items.

Walt's Fish Market • 4144 S. Tamiami Trl. • 921-4605
WHAT YOU CAN FIND THERE: Huge selection of fresh local fish & seafood. Stone crabs when in season. Smoked mullet spread!

KOJO
1289 North Palm Avenue
941-536-9717
eatkojo.com

DOWNTOWN	ASIAN	COST: $$$

HOURS: Sun-Thur, 4PM to 11PM
Fri & Sat, 4PM to 12AM

WHAT TO EXPECT: Upscale Asian Cuisine • Ramen, Sushi & Bao Buns
Next To Palm Ave Garage • Online Reservations

BEST BITES: Wasabi Caesar Salad • Crispy Tofu Bites
Truffled Chicken Wontons • Torched Salmon Nori Taco
Bao Buns • Wagyu Skirt Steak • Sushi

SOME BASICS

SCAN FOR MENU

Reservations:	YES
Spirits:	FULL BAR
Parking:	GARAGE/STREET
Outdoor Dining:	YES

KOLUCAN

NEW

6644 Gateway Avenue
941-921-3133
kolucan.com

GULF GATE	MEXICAN	COST: $$$

HOURS: Lunch, Mon-Fri, 11AM to 3PM
Dinner, Mon-Sat, 5PM to 10PM • CLOSED SUNDAY

WHAT TO EXPECT: "Elevated Mexican Flavors" • The Frida Lounge
Upscale Dining • Great Outdoor Dining Space

BEST BITES: Elote Asado • Street Tacos • Ensalada de Berros
Tortas Planchadas • Huitlachoche Risotto
Enchiladas Divorciadas • Seasonal Red Sangria

SCAN FOR MENU

SOME BASICS

Reservations:	YES
Spirits:	FULL BAR
Parking:	LOT
Outdoor Dining:	YES

KORÊ STEAKHOUSE

1561 Lakefront Drive
941-928-5673
koresteakhouse.com

WATERSIDE PLACE	KOREAN	COST: $$$

HOURS: Open Daily, Lunch & Dinner

WHAT TO EXPECT: REAL Korean Bbq • Super Upscale Feel
Busy For Dinner • Fun For Groups

BEST BITES: Bulgogi Mandoo • Egg Souffle • Japchae Noodles
Dolsot Bibimbap • Kimchi Jjigae • Cheese Corn
Beef, Pork, Seafood, Chicken & Veggie Grilling Items

SCAN FOR MENU

SOME BASICS

Reservations:	NO
Spirits:	BEER/WINE
Parking:	STREET
Outdoor Dining:	NO

LA DOLCE VITA

2704 Stickney Point Road
941-210-3631
ladolcevitasarasota.com

ITALIAN	**COST: $$$**

HOURS: Tue-Sat, 5PM TO 9PM
CLOSED SUNDAY & MONDAY

WHAT TO EXPECT: Southern & Northern Italian Cuisine
Nice Wine List • Online Reservations

BEST BITES: Cozze Alla Marinara • Insalata Favolosa
Scialatielli, Gamberi E Asparagi • Gnocchi Alla Sorrentina
Misto Partenopeo • Petto Di Pollo Alla Siciliana

SOME BASICS

SCAN FOR MENU

Reservations:	YES
Spirits:	BEER/WINE
Parking:	LOT
Outdoor Dining:	NO

THE LAZY LOBSTER

5350 Gulf of Mexico Drive
941-383-0440
lazylobsteroflongboat.com

LONGBOAT KEY	**SEAFOOD**	**COST: $$$**

HOURS: Mon-Sat, 11AM to 9PM
CLOSED SUNDAY

WHAT TO EXPECT: Great Casual Seafood • Early Dining Menu

BEST BITES: Chilled Ahi Tuna • Lobster Scargot • Lobster Bisque
Hot Fried Chicken Salad • The Open Faced Reuben
Stuffed Shrimp "Norma" • Lobster Mac & Cheese

SOME BASICS

SCAN FOR MENU

Reservations:	YES
Spirits:	FULL BAR
Parking:	LOT
Outdoor Dining:	YES

LIBBY'S NEIGHBORHOOD BRASSERIE

1917 South Osprey Avenue*
941-487-7300
libbysneighborhoodbrasserie.com

SOUTHSIDE VILLAGE	AMERICAN	COST: $$$

HOURS: Sun-Thur, 11AM to 9PM
Fri & Sat, 11AM to 10PM

WHAT TO EXPECT: Upscale Dining Experience • Good Wine List
Busy Bar Scene • Reservations A Must During Season

BEST BITES: Tuna Taki • Avocado Eggrolls • Kale Caesar Salad
Krabby Patty Sandwich • Meatball Smash Sandwich
Louisiana Chicken Pasta • Dr. Pepper Ribs

SCAN FOR MENU

SOME BASICS

Reservations:	YES
Spirits:	FULL BAR
Parking:	LOT/STREET
Outdoor Dining:	YES

LILA

1576 Main Street
941-296-1042
lilasrq.com

DOWNTOWN	AMERICAN	COST: $$

HOURS: Mon-Fri, 11AM to 9PM • Sat, 10:30AM to 9PM
CLOSED SUNDAY

WHAT TO EXPECT: Organic, Locally Sourced Menu • Lighter Fare
Opentable Reservations • Lots Of Veg/Vegan Options

BEST BITES: Vegan Sushi Rolls • Roasted Yam Wedges
Red Beet, Apple, Orange Salad • Mushroom Burger
Ramen Noodle Bowl • Verlasso Salmon

SCAN FOR MENU

SOME BASICS

Reservations:	YES
Spirits:	BEER/WINE
Parking:	STREET
Outdoor Dining:	NO

LOBSTER POT

5157 Ocean Boulevard
941-349-2323
sarasotalobsterpot.com

SIESTA KEY	SEAFOOD	COST: $$

HOURS: Mon-Thur, 11:30AM to 9PM • Fri & Sat, 11:30AM to 9:30PM
CLOSED SUNDAY

WHAT TO EXPECT: Great For Families • Lobster ++ • Siesta Village
Good For Kids

BEST BITES: Kettle of Mussels • Broiled Fiery Scallops
Portuguese Soup • Watermelon Salad • Lazy Dutchess
Alaskan King Crab • Salmon Rockefeller • Filet Mignon

SOME BASICS

SCAN FOR MENU

Reservations:	6 OR MORE
Spirits:	BEER/WINE
Parking:	VALET/STREET
Outdoor Dining:	YES

LOBSTERCRAFT

St. Armands Circle
941-346-6325
lobstercraft.com

ST ARMANDS	SEAFOOD	COST: $$$

HOURS: Tues-Sun, 11AM to 8PM
CLOSED MONDAY

WHAT TO EXPECT: Super Casual Atmosphere • Great For A Carryout
Busy Area During Season

BEST BITES: Lobster Bisque • Clam Chowder • Lobster Tacos
Lots of Lobster Roll Choices • Lobster Mac n Cheese

SOME BASICS

SCAN FOR MENU

Reservations:	NO
Spirits:	BEER/WINE
Parking:	STREET/GARAGE
Outdoor Dining:	YES

LOVELY SQUARE

6559 Gateway Avenue
941-724-2512
lovelysquareflorida.com

GULF GATE	AMERICAN	COST: $$

HOURS: Mon-Sun, 8AM to 2PM
CLOSED TUESDAY

WHAT TO EXPECT: Casual Dining Spot • Nice Selection Of Crepes
Good For Families • Easy On The Wallet

BEST BITES: Classic Eggs Benedict • Omelets & Frittatas
Morning Crepe • Banana Nut Pancakes
Greek Salad • Club B.E.L.T. • Baguette Brie Chicken

SCAN FOR MENU

SOME BASICS

Reservations:	NO
Spirits:	BEER/WINE
Parking:	LOT
Outdoor Dining:	NO

LYNCHES PUB AND GRUB

19 North Boulevard of Presidents
941-388-5550
lynches.pub

ST ARMANDS	IRISH	COST: $$

HOURS: Mon-Sat, 11AM to 12AM
Sunday, 12PM to 10PM

WHAT TO EXPECT: Irish Pub Fare • Over 100 Irish Whiskeys
Beer, Wine & Liquor To-Go • Established 2003!

BEST BITES: Breakfast Anytime! • "Irish" Chicken Egg Rolls
St. Armands Salad • Fish & Chips • Cottage Pie
Corned Beef & Cabbage • Key Lime Pie

SCAN FOR MENU

SOME BASICS

Reservations:	NO
Spirits:	FULL BAR
Parking:	STREET/GARAGE
Outdoor Dining:	YES

THE MABLE

2831 North Tamiami Trail
941-487-7373

NORTH TRAIL	AMERICAN	COST: $$

HOURS: Daily, 4PM to 2AM

WHAT TO EXPECT: Fantastic "Dive" Bar • Ringling College Students
Great Burger! • Lots of Craft Beer to Choose From

BEST BITES: The Burger! • Poutine • Grilled Steak Tacos
Truffle Tater Tots • Vegetarian Chili • Potstickers
Fried Buffalo Chicken Sammy • Warm Bavarian Pretzel

SOME BASICS

MORE INFO

Reservations:	NO
Spirits:	FULL BAR
Parking:	LOT
Outdoor Dining:	YES

MADE

1990 Main Street
941-953-2900
maderestaurant.com

DOWNTOWN	AMERICAN	COST: $$

HOURS: Tue-Fri, Lunch, 11:30AM to 2:30PM • Sun, 10AM to 2PM
Tue-Sat, Dinner, 5PM to 10PM • CLOSED MONDAY

WHAT TO EXPECT: Great For A Date • Upscale American Cuisine
Chef Driven Menu

BEST BITES: Cheesy Tots • Disco Fries • MADE Mac-n-Cheese
Smoked Chicken Taco Salad • Double Dipped Fried Chicken
MADE Burger • Short Rib Philly • "Four" Meatloaf

SOME BASICS

SCAN FOR MENU

Reservations:	YES
Spirits:	FULL BAR
Parking:	STREET/GARAGE
Outdoor Dining:	YES

Urbanek's Original Steamship Pot

Pop's Sunset Grill

INGREDIENTS

2 tablespoons olive oil
1 yellow onion thinly sliced
2 garlic heads, split in half
Salt and pepper
4 oz. Old Bay seasoning
1-2 quarts of water
12 oz of beer
1/2 pound celery cut into 3 inch pieces
1/2 pound carrots cut into 3 inch pieces
1 pound medium red potatoes, quartered
1 pound andouille sausage, cut into 3-inch pieces
1 pound mussels
1 pound 26/30 shell-on shrimp
4 ears corn, husked and cut in half
Parsley chopped for garnish
Lemon wedges for garnish

METHOD

In a large stockpot over medium heat, add the olive oil. Add the onions, garlic, and pepper, and season with salt. Reduce the heat to medium low and cook, stirring often, until the onions are soft but haven't browned too much, 6 to 8 minutes.

Add 1-2 quarts of water, 12 oz of beer and Old Bay seasoning, bring to a boil.

Add potatoes, carrots, celery, corn, and season with more salt. Decrease the heat and cook at a high simmer until the potatoes are almost tender, 20 to 25 minutes depending on the size.

Add the sausage, nestling each piece into the broth. Top with the mussels, and shrimp . Cover and cook until the mussels begin to open and shrimp turn pink, 10 to 15 minutes.

Using a slotted spoon, divide the mussels, shrimp, sausage, and vegetables into bowls. Ladle the broth into each bowl and sprinkle chopped parsley over the top. Serve with lemon wedges and drawn butter for dipping.

** The Urbanek's Original Steamship pot is a signature item that has been part of the Pop's menu since 1954. We have modified the recipe slightly for the home cook.

Pop's Sunset Grill was born as a combination of Pop's and Urbanek's Fish Camp, dating back to 1954. Twenty-two years ago, the owners combined the restaurants to the single name, Pop's Sunset Grill. The "Old Florida Fish Camp Vibe" of the South Bar (one of three bars at Pop's!) still retains the 1954 Fish Camp vibe. With the addition of the 3-level tiki bar, this waterfront destination truly offers something for everyone. Pop's Sunset Grill remains one of the Gulf Coast's favorite waterfront dining landmarks, well loved by locals and tourists alike for its casual atmosphere, fresh local fare, daily live music, and the constant parade of boats and dolphins.

 # SARASOTA SEAFOOD MARKETS

Big Water Fish Market • 6641 Midnight Pass Rd. • 554-8101
WHAT YOU CAN FIND THERE: Fresh Florida fish. Great prepared seafood items. Just south of Siesta Key's south bridge.

Morton's Gourmet Market • 1924 S. Osprey Ave. • 955-9856
WHAT YOU CAN FIND THERE: Upscale gourmet food items including a nice selection of fresh seafood and meat. Great deli & carryout.

Walt's Fish Market • 4144 S. Tamiami Trl. • 921-4605
WHAT YOU CAN FIND THERE: Huge selection of fresh local fish & seafood. Stone crabs when in season. Smoked mullet spread!

MADEMOISELLE PARIS

8527 Cooper Creek Boulevard*
941-355-2323
mademoiselleparis.com

LWR	FRENCH	COST: $$

HOURS: Mon & Tue, 7:45AM to 5PM
Wed-Sun, 7:45AM to 9PM

WHAT TO EXPECT: Traditional French Fare • Casual European Dining
Tartines, Omlettes And More!

BEST BITES: Tartine Gourmande • Omelettes • Quiche Lorraine
Croque Madame • Beef Burgundy • French Onion Soup
Crepes! • Profiteroles • Crême Brulée

SCAN FOR MENU

SOME BASICS

Reservations:	YES
Spirits:	BEER/WINE
Parking:	LOT
Outdoor Dining:	YES

MADFISH GRILL

4059 Cattleman Road
941-377-3474
madfishgrill.com

	SEAFOOD	COST: $$

HOURS: Mon-Sat, 11:30AM to 9PM • Sun, 11AM to 8PM
Sunday Brunch, 11AM to 2PM

WHAT TO EXPECT: Good For Families • Daily Specials
Happy Hour Bites Menu • Sunday Brunch Menu

BEST BITES: Chicken Cobb Salad • Bang Shrimp Bowl
Drunken Lobster Bisque • Blackened Grouper Sandwich
Tacos • Pan Seared Cod • Abuela's House-made Flan

SCAN FOR MENU

SOME BASICS

Reservations:	YES
Spirits:	FULL BAR
Parking:	LOT
Outdoor Dining:	YES

MAIN BAR SANDWICH SHOP

1944 Main Street
941-955-8733
themainbar.com

DOWNTOWN	DELI	COST: $

HOURS: Mon-Sat, 10AM to 4PM
CLOSED SUNDAY

WHAT TO EXPECT: Great For Quick Lunch • Easy On The Wallet
Lively Atmosphere • Fantastic Service

BEST BITES: Famous Italian Sandwich • New Yorker Sandwich
Homemade Soups • Tuna Salad Plate • Sultan Salad
Sarasotan Wrap • Key Lime Pie

SOME BASICS

SCAN FOR MENU

Reservations:	NO
Spirits:	BEER/WINE
Parking:	STREET
Outdoor Dining:	NO

MAISON BLANCHE

2605 Gulf of Mexico Drive (Four Winds Beach Resort)
941-383-8088
themaisonblanche.com

LONGBOAT KEY	FRENCH	COST: $$$$

HOURS: Wed-Sun, 5:30PM to 9:30PM
CLOSED MONDAY & TUESDAY

WHAT TO EXPECT: Date Night! • Special Occasions
Excellent Service • Great Wine List • Online Reservations

BEST BITES: Wild Mushroom Raviolis With Foie Gras Sauce
Chanterelles Risotto • Tomato Tart • Red Snapper
Beef Short Ribs • Chocolate Souffle With Creme Anglaise

SOME BASICS

SCAN FOR MENU

Reservations:	YES
Spirits:	BEER/WINE
Parking:	LOT
Outdoor Dining:	NO

MALMOSTO WINE SHOP & KITCHEN

2085 Siesta Drive
941-706-1460
wineshopandkitchen.com

SOUTHGATE	ITALIAN	COST: $$$

HOURS: Mon-Sat, 5PM to Close
CLOSED SUNDAY

WHAT TO EXPECT: Cozy Indoor Dining Space • Italian Pizza
Great Hand-Curated Wine Selection • Chef Andrea Bozzolo

BEST BITES: Porketta • Boneless Short Ribs • Candele Spezzate Pasta
Seafood Paella • Pacific Blue Fin Tuna Dome
Lots of Delicious Pizzas to Choose From

SCAN FOR MENU

SOME BASICS

Reservations:	YES
Spirits:	FULL BAR
Parking:	LOT
Outdoor Dining:	NO

MAR VISTA DOCKSIDE RESTAURANT & PUB

760 Broadway Street
941-383-2391
marvistadining.com

LONGBOAT KEY	AMERICAN	COST: $$

HOURS: Sun-Thur, 11:30AM to 9PM
Fri & Sat, 11:30AM to 10PM

WHAT TO EXPECT: Great For Families • Big List Of Specialty Drinks
Water View • Old Florida Feel • 14 Private Slips For Boaters

BEST BITES: Fish Dip • Beer & Old Bay Shrimp • Crab Cake Trio
Seafood Gumbo • Cobia Burger • Seafood Paella
Chef's Boil Pot • Coconut Cake

SCAN FOR MENU

SOME BASICS

Reservations:	NO
Spirits:	FULL BAR
Parking:	LOT
Outdoor Dining:	YES

MARCELLO'S RISTORANTE

4155 South Tamiami Trail
941-921-6794
marcellosarasota.com

SOUTH TRAIL	ITALIAN	COST: $$$

HOURS: Tue-Sat, 5:30PM to 9PM
CLOSED SUNDAY & MONDAY

WHAT TO EXPECT: Nice Wine List • Chef Driven Italian Cuisine
Small & Intimate Dining Experience

BEST BITES: Grilled Octopus • Beef Carpaccio • Lamb Ragu
Braised Beef Short Ribs • Diver Sea Scallops
Hudson Valley Duck Breast • Tiramisu • Cannoli

SOME BASICS

SCAN FOR INFO

Reservations: YES
Spirits: BEER/WINE
Parking: LOT
Outdoor Dining: NO

MARINA JACK'S

2 Marina Plaza
941-365-4232
marinajacks.com

DOWNTOWN	SEAFOOD	COST: $$$

HOURS: Sun-Thur, 11AM to 9PM
Fri & Sat, 11AM to 10PM

WHAT TO EXPECT: Water View • Dinner Cruises • Live Music
Nice Wine List • Live Music • Outdoor Lounge

BEST BITES: Filet Mignon Center Cut • Prawn Martini
Charcuterie Board • Sherry Crab Bisque • Mahi Francaise
Pan Seared Scallops • Bouillabaisse • Lump Crab Cakes

SOME BASICS

SCAN FOR MENU

Reservations: YES
Spirits: FULL BAR
Parking: VALET/LOT
Outdoor Dining: YES

MATTISON'S CITY GRILLE

1 North Lemon Avenue
941-330-0440
mattisons.com

DOWNTOWN	AMERICAN	COST: $$

HOURS: Lunch - Daily, 11AM to 3PM
Dinner - Daily, 4:30PM to 10PM

WHAT TO EXPECT: Great For A Date • Downtown Meet-Up Spot
Live Music • Great Bar Service • Happy Hour Daily

BEST BITES: Tuna Poke Tower • NE Clam Chowder • Shakshuka
Niman Ranch Reuben • Brick Oven Pizza!
Seafood Gumbo • Grouper Piccata • Key Lime Pie

SCAN FOR MENU

SOME BASICS

Reservations:	YES
Spirits:	FULL BAR
Parking:	STREET
Outdoor Dining:	YES

MATTISON'S FORTY ONE

7275 South Tamiami Trail
941-921-3400
mattisons.com

SOUTH TRAIL	AMERICAN	COST: $$

HOURS: Mon-Thur, 11:30AM to 9PM • Fri, 11:30AM to 10PM
Sat, 4:30PM to 10PM • CLOSED SUNDAY

WHAT TO EXPECT: Large Wine List • Brunch • Good Value
Online Reservations • Happy Hour Menu

BEST BITES: Artichokes Esther-Style • Wedge Salad • Pork Belly
Forty-One Burger • Rack Of Lamb • Fish & Chips
Maple Leaf Farms Duck • Thai Soba Noodle Bowl

SCAN FOR MENU

SOME BASICS

Reservations:	YES
Spirits:	FULL BAR
Parking:	LOT
Outdoor Dining:	NO

MEAN DEANS LOCAL KITCHEN

6059 26th Street W
941-251-5435
meandeanslocalkitchen.com

BRADENTON	AMERICAN	COST: $$$

HOURS: Sun-Thur, 11AM to 9PM
Fri & Sat, 11AM to 10PM

WHAT TO EXPECT: Catering Available
Locally Sourced Ingredients • Good Wine List

BEST BITES: Deconstructed Goat Cheese Bruschetta
Calamari & Peppers • Candied Bacon Bleu
Pork Osso Bucco • Lobster Lasagna • Brooklyn Ice Cream

SOME BASICS

Reservations:	YES
Spirits:	FULL BAR
Parking:	LOT
Outdoor Dining:	NO

SCAN FOR MENU

Keep Up With Your Favorite Sarasota Restaurants

FOLLOW, LIKE & SUBSCRIBE
DineSarasota

MEDITERRANEO
1970 Main Street
941-365-4122
mediterraneorest.com

DOWNTOWN	ITALIAN	COST: $$

HOURS: Lunch, Mon-Fri, 11:30AM to 2:30PM
Dinner, Daily from 5:30PM

WHAT TO EXPECT: Pizza • Good Wine List • Italian Specialties
Online Reservations • Private Party Dining Space

BEST BITES: Carpaccio Rucola • Mista Salad • Gamberi Salad
Minestrone Soup • Linguine Mare • Pollo Milanese
Paninis • Le Pizze Classiche • Profiteroles

SCAN FOR MENU

SOME BASICS

Reservations:	YES
Spirits:	FULL BAR
Parking:	STREET/GARAGE
Outdoor Dining:	YES

MARCEL
NEW

1568 Main Street
941-953-7111
melangesarasota.com

DOWNTOWN	AMERICAN	COST: $$$

HOURS: Wed-Sun, 5PM-10PM
CLOSED MONDAY & TUESDAY

WHAT TO EXPECT: "New" American Cuisine • Small Plates
Perfect For Date Night • Sophisticated Menu Options

BEST BITES: Steak Tartare • Snapper Ceviche • Mortadella Toast
Braised Beef Short Ribs • Peppered Salmon • Squab
Key Lime Pie • Marcel Creme Brulee

SCAN FOR MENU

SOME BASICS

Reservations:	YES
Spirits:	FULL BAR
Parking:	STREET
Outdoor Dining:	YES

MELIORA

1920 Hillview Street
941-444-7692
meliorarestaurant.com

SOUTHSIDE VILLAGE	AMERICAN	COST: $$$$

HOURS: Tues-Sat, 5PM to 9PM
CLOSED SUNDAY & MONDAY

WHAT TO EXPECT: Very Upscale Dining • Creative "Chef Driven" Menu
Reservations A Must • Chef's Table Seating Available

BEST BITES: Cold Menu Items - Raw Scallop, Cold Pork, Cucumber
Hot Menu Items - Fried Potato, Scamp Grouper, Gnocchi
Dessert Items - Japanese Cheesecake, Tomato Sorbet

SOME BASICS

SCAN FOR MENU

Reservations:	YES
Spirits:	FULL BAR
Parking:	STREET
Outdoor Dining:	NO

MESHUGANA DELI

NEW

4001 Clark Road
941-933-0244
meshuganasrq.com

	DELI	COST: $$

HOURS: Mon-Fri, 10AM to 6PM • Sat, 10AM to 3PM
CLOSED SUNDAY

WHAT TO EXPECT: NY Style Deli • Catering & Platters Available
Super Casual Atmosphere • Lots of Parking

BEST BITES: Brisket Sandwich • Corned Beef Sandwich
Turkey Reuben • Potato Knish • Latkes
Macaroons and Black & White Cookies

SOME BASICS

SCAN FOR MENU

Reservations:	NO
Spirits:	NONE
Parking:	LOT
Outdoor Dining:	YES

MICHAEL'S ON EAST

1212 East Avenue South
941-366-0007
bestfood.com

MIDTOWN PLAZA	AMERICAN	COST: $$$

HOURS: Tue-Thur, 5PM to 8:30PM • Fri & Sat, 5PM to 9PM
CLOSED SUNDAY AND MONDAY

WHAT TO EXPECT: Piano Lounge • Catering • Fine Dining
Opentable Reservations • AAA Four Diamond Award

BEST BITES: Lobster & Escargots • Mussels Marinière
East Avenue Caesar • Colony Snapper • Duck Two-Ways
Michael's Famous Bowtie Pasta • Brownie Ice Cream Stack

SCAN FOR MENU

SOME BASICS

Reservations:	YES
Spirits:	FULL BAR
Parking:	VALET
Outdoor Dining:	YES

MICHELLE'S BROWN BAG CAFÉ

630 North Orange Avenue
941-365-5858
michellesbrownbagcafe.com

DOWNTOWN	DELI	COST: $

HOURS: Mon-Fri, 9AM to 2PM
CLOSED SATURDAY & SUNDAY

WHAT TO EXPECT: Quick Lunch • Easy On The Wallet
Great Meet-Up Spot • Super Casual

BEST BITES: Longboat Brie Sandwich • Bayfront Tuna Sandwich
Farmer's Market Salad • Paninis • Lox & Bagel
Turkey Reuben • Half Sandwich + Soup!

SCAN FOR MENU

SOME BASICS

Reservations:	NO
Spirits:	BEER/WINE
Parking:	GARAGE/STREET
Outdoor Dining:	NO

MIGUEL'S

6631 Midnight Pass Road
941-349-4024
miguelsrestaurant.net

SIESTA KEY	FRENCH	COST: $$$

HOURS: Dinner, Daily from 4PM
Early Dinner Menu, 4PM to 6PM

WHAT TO EXPECT: Good Wine List • Quiet Atmosphere
Good Early Dining Menu • Nice For A Date

BEST BITES: Les Escargot Bourgogne • Steak Tartare
Sopa De Ajo • Les Fruits De Mer • Moules Normandy
Le Chateaubriand Bouquetiere • Le Veau Piccata

SOME BASICS

SCAN FOR MENU

Reservations:	YES
Spirits:	FULL BAR
Parking:	LOT
Outdoor Dining:	NO

MOLLY'S RESTAURANT & PUB

1562 Main Street
941-366-7711
eviesonline.com/location/mollys-pub

DOWNTOWN	IRISH	COST: $$

HOURS: Tues-Sat, 4PM to 10PM
CLOSED SUNDAY & MONDAY

WHAT TO EXPECT: Fun Pub Atmosphere • Downtown Location
Special Events • Great After Work Meetup Spot

BEST BITES: Shepherd's Pie • Bangers & Mash • Reuben
Cobb Salad • Hot Ham & Cheese • Deviled Eggs
Salmon BLT • Molly's Burger • Grilled Wings

SOME BASICS

SCAN FOR MENU

Reservations:	NO
Spirits:	FULL BAR
Parking:	STREET/GARAGE
Outdoor Dining:	YES

TZEVA

MODERN MEDITERRANEAN CUISINE

Make it at
HOME

Pickled Watermelon Rinds

Tzeva
Executive Chef Ken Shiro Lumpkin

INGREDIENTS
2 pounds of watermelon rinds
½ cup Korean apple vinegar
½ cup lime juice
½ cup rice wine vinegar
½ cup white wine vinegar
¾ cup sugar
½ cup mirin
1 cup water
2 tbsp salt
Large knuckle of ginger, sliced
1 tbsp allspice
1 cinnamon stick
3 Makrut lime leaf
3 star anise pods
4 cloves, whole
2 bay leaf
2 cloves of garlic, crushed

METHOD
Peel the dark green skin off the watermelon rind, cut into 1/4"
slices.

Put all the ingredients, but the rinds, into a large pot.
Bring to a boil, turn heat down to a simmer and reduce liquid by
20%.

Add rinds and cook until the rinds are translucent (about 45 minutes).Transfer the liquid and rinds to a jar and allow it to cool slowly at room temperature. Store in the fridge for up to a month.

Journey to the Mediterranean by way of taste buds at Tzeva, nestled inside the Art Ovation Hotel Autograph Collection. Tzeva features modern Mediterranean cuisine with Israeli influences that shine in beautifully plated dishes full of bright colors, unique flavors, and global spices. The menu reflects a culinary artistry that shifts with the seasons and features a style of dining that encourages the sharing and passing of plates to create a sense of community around the table. Tzeva is open for breakfast, lunch, and dinner.

Join the other 18,000+ Follow us on Facebook!

dineSarasota

18K followers • 588 following

MONK'S STEAMER BAR

6690 Superior Avenue
941-927-3388
monkssteamerbar.com

GULF GATE	SEAFOOD	COST: $$

HOURS: Mon-Thur, 3PM to 12AM • Fri & Sat, 12PM to 1AM
Sunday, 12PM to 12AM

WHAT TO EXPECT: Steamed Everything! • Dive Bar/Great Food
Locals Favorite • Late Night Menu

BEST BITES: Seafood Bisque • Oysters Monkafeller • Mussels
Cajun Crawfish • Peel N Eat Shrimp • Oyster Shooters!

SOME BASICS

Reservations:	NO
Spirits:	FULL BAR
Parking:	STREET/LOT
Outdoor Dining:	NO

SCAN FOR MENU

MUNCHIES 420 CAFÉ
6639 Superior Avenue
941-929-9893
munchies420cafe.com

GULF GATE	AMERICAN	COST: $$

HOURS: Sun-Thur, 12PM to 3AM • Fri & Sat, 12PM to 4:20AM
Happy Hour, Daily, 12PM to 7PM

WHAT TO EXPECT: Crazy Sandwiches! • Super Laid Back • Late Night
Local Favorite

BEST BITES: Covered Spuds • Mac & Cheezadilla • OG Philly Works
Blazed Crispy Chicken • Super HOT Wings • Fat Sandy
The Humongo Burger • Fried Twinkies • Nice Krispy Treats

SCAN FOR MENU

SOME BASICS
Reservations:	NO
Spirits:	FULL BAR
Parking:	LOT
Outdoor Dining:	YES

---

99 BOTTLES TAPROOM
1445 Second Street
941-487-7874
99bottles.net

DOWNTOWN	BEER	COST: $$

HOURS: Mon-Thur, 3PM to 11PM
Fri-Sun, 9AM to 12AM

WHAT TO EXPECT: Big City Feel • Knowledgeable Bar Staff
"Pop-Up" Dining Events • Great For An After Work Beer

BEST BITES: NY Bagel Brunch (Weekends)
Classic Hummus • Soft Pretzel • Short Rib Flatbread
Truffle Popcorn • Charcuterie Boards

SCAN FOR MENU

SOME BASICS
Reservations:	NO
Spirits:	BEER/WINE
Parking:	STREET/GARAGE
Outdoor Dining:	YES

NAMO IZAKAYA

1439 Main Street
941-362-3332
namoizakaya.com

DOWNTOWN	ASIAN	COST: $$

HOURS: Daily, 11AM to 10PM

WHAT TO EXPECT: Casual Japanese Cuisine • Main St. Location
Small But Mighty Menu

BEST BITES: Sweet Corn Cheese • Namo Fried Chicken
Hijiki Seaweed Salad • Tonkotsu Ramen
Salmon Teriyaki • Unagi • Creamy Curry

SOME BASICS

SCAN FOR MENU

Reservations:	YES
Spirits:	BEER/WINE
Parking:	STREET
Outdoor Dining:	YES

NANCY'S BAR-B-QUE

1525 Fourth Street
941-999-2390
nancysbarbq.com

LWR	BBQ	COST: $

HOURS: Mon-Thur, 11AM to 9PM • Fri & Sat, 11AM to 10PM
Sunday, 11AM to 8OM

WHAT TO EXPECT: Casual Dining • Good For Families
Catering Available • Combo Meals • Great Pulled Pork!

BEST BITES: Pulled Pork & Chicken • Beef Brisket • Ribs
Combo Trays (Texas Holy Trinity) • Smoked Sausage
Brisket "Interstate Cheesesteak" • Baked Mac N Cheese

SOME BASICS

SCAN FOR MENU

Reservations:	NO
Spirits:	FULLBAR
Parking:	LOT
Outdoor Dining:	YES

SARASOTA
UPSCALE CHAIN DINING

Sarasota has a ton of great independently owned and operated restaurants. And, that's mostly what this dining book is all about. But, as with any decent sized city, we've got our share of quality, upscale chain dining options, too.

We've taken the time to put together a list of some of our favorites. Just like the main section of the book, we didn't have the space to list them all. So, we curated a collection of the ones we think will give you a consistent and favorable dining experience.

We've tried to include a little bit of everything here for you. Some steakhouses, sushi, deli, and even pizza. You'll recognize most of the names, I'm sure. There's something here for everyone.

Bonefish Grill • 3971 S. Tamiami Trl. • 924-9090
WHAT TO EXPECT: Upscale casual place to meet up with friends and enjoy drinks or dinner. Lots of seafood options. ($$)

Brio Tuscan Grille • 190 University Town Center Dr. • 702-9102
WHAT TO EXPECT: Italian cuisine. UTC. Online reservations. Lively atmosphere. Good for groups. ($$$)

Cooper's Hawk • 3130 Fruitville Commons Blvd. • 263-8100
WHAT TO EXPECT: Steaks, seafood, much more. Fantastic wine selection. Modern, casual dining. ($$$)

Capital Grille • 180 University Town Center Dr. • 256-3647
WHAT TO EXPECT: Big city steakhouse. Very upscale dining experience. Reservations/OpenTable. Private dining. ($$$$)

Chart House • 201 Gulf of Mexico Dr. • 383-5593
WHAT TO EXPECT: Fresh seafood. Nice gulf view. Always outstanding service. Classic upscale dining experience. ($$$)

Cheesecake Factory • 130 University Town Center Dr. • 256-3760
WHAT TO EXPECT: 200+ menu choices. Super large portions. Happy Hour. Catering. Very busy dining atmosphere. ($$$)

Fleming's Prime Steakhouse • 2001 Siesta Dr. • 358-9463
WHAT TO EXPECT: Super high quality steaks + service. Private dining. "Fleming's 100" wines. Happy Hour. ($$$$)

Hyde Park Steakhouse • 35 S. Lemon Ave. • 366-7788
WHAT TO EXPECT: Busy downtown location. Valet parking. Popular Happy Hour. "Early Nights" menu. Private dining. ($$$$)

Kona Grill • 150 University Town Center Dr. • 256-8050
WHAT TO EXPECT: Heavy Asian influence cuisine. Sushi. Lively dining experience. UTC Mall. Online reservations. ($$)

P.F. Chang's Bistro • 766 S. Osprey Ave. • 296-6002
WHAT TO EXPECT: "Farm to Wok" Asian cuisine. Large menu. Busy, vibrant atmosphere. Good for groups. Online reservations. ($$$)

Rodizio Brazilian Steakhouse • 5911 Fruitville Rd. • 260-8445
WHAT TO EXPECT: Brazilian steakhouse experience. Rotisserie grilled meats. Tableside service. Large gourmet salad bar. ($$$)

Ruth's Chris Steakhouse • 6700 S. Tamiami Trl. • 942-8982
WHAT TO EXPECT: Exceptional service. Older dining crowd. Large selection of USDA prime steaks. Great wine list. ($$$$)

Seasons 52 • 170 University Town Center Dr. • 702-5652
WHAT TO EXPECT: Seasonal menu selections. 52 wines by the glass. UTC Mall. Group dining options. Great service. ($$$)

Sophie's • 120 University Town Center Dr. • 444-3077
WHAT TO EXPECT: UTC inside Saks FIfth Avenue. "Ladies" lunch spot. Intimate dining experience. Great for private parties. ($$$)

NAPULÈ RISTORANTE ITALIANO

7129 South Tamiami Trail
941-556-9639
napulesarasota.com

SOUTH TRAIL	ITALIAN	COST: $$$

HOURS: Mon-Thur, 11:30AM to 9:30PM
Fri & Sat, 11:30AM to 10:30PM • CLOSED SUNDAY

WHAT TO EXPECT: Upscale Italian Dining • Great Wood Oven Pizza
Very Busy In Season • Vibrant Atmosphere

BEST BITES: Salumeria • Burrata • Bufala Salad • Fresella Salad
Trio di Bruschette • Polipetti Alla Luciana
Saltimbocca Di Vitello Alla Romana • Pizza!

SCAN FOR MENU

SOME BASICS

Reservations:	YES
Spirits:	FULL BAR
Parking:	LOT
Outdoor Dining:	YES

NEW PASS GRILL & BAIT SHOP

1505 Ken Thompson Parkway
941-388-3050
newpassgrill.com

CITY ISLAND	AMERICAN	COST: $

HOURS: Daily, 7AM to 7PM

WHAT TO EXPECT: Casual Dining • Water View • More Than Burgers
Bait & Tackle Shop • A "Landmark" Since 1929

BEST BITES: Breakfast! • NE Clam Chowder • BLT
Hot Dog or Polish Sausage • New Pass Burgers
Fried Chicken Sandwich • Fish N Chips • Ice Cream Bar!

SCAN FOR MENU

SOME BASICS

Reservations:	NO
Spirits:	BEER/WINE
Parking:	LOT
Outdoor Dining:	YES

OAK & STONE

5405 University Parkway*
941-225-4590
oakandstone.com

UPARK	AMERICAN	COST: $$

HOURS: Sun-Thur, 11AM to 10PM
Fri & Sat, 11AM to 12AM

WHAT TO EXPECT: Great For Sports Viewing • Lively Atmosphere
Live Music • Large Beer Selection • Pizza Too!

BEST BITES: Philly Cheesesteak Egg Rolls • Beer Cheese Soup
Buffalo Chicken Bowl • Pizza! • Crispy Grouper BLT
Classic Reuben • Griddle Burger

SOME BASICS

SCAN FOR MENU

Reservations:	NO
Spirits:	FULL BAR
Parking:	LOT
Outdoor Dining:	YES

OASIS CAFÉ & BAKERY

3542 South Osprey Avenue
941-957-1214
theoasiscafe.net

	AMERICAN	COST: $$

HOURS: Tue-Fri, 7AM to 2PM • Sat & Sun, 8AM to 1:30PM
CLOSED MONDAY

WHAT TO EXPECT: Breakfast & Lunch • Casual Dining
Great Daily Specials • Homemade Pastries & Baked Goods

BEST BITES: Eggs Benedict • Cheese Blintzes • Lox & Bagel
Italian Scramble • Blackened Basa Reuben
Soup & Salad Combo • Siesta Sister Wrap

SOME BASICS

SCAN FOR MENU

Reservations:	NO
Spirits:	BEER/WINE
Parking:	LOT
Outdoor Dining:	YES

THE OLD SALTY DOG

5023 Ocean Boulevard*
941-349-0158
theoldsaltydog.com

SIESTA KEY	AMERICAN	COST: $$

HOURS: Daily, 11AM to 9PM

WHAT TO EXPECT: Locals Love It • Vacation Feel • Cold Beer
As Seen On TV! • Great For Families

BEST BITES: Hand-Cut Onion Rings • Peel N Eat Shrimp
NE Clam Chowder • The Famous "Salty Dog"
Grouper Reuben • Firecracker Wrap • Fish 'N Chips

SCAN FOR MENU

SOME BASICS

Reservations:	NO
Spirits:	FULL BAR
Parking:	STREET
Outdoor Dining:	YES

O'LEARY'S TIKI BAR & GRILL

5 Bayfront Drive
941-953-7505
olearystikibar.com

DOWNTOWN	AMERICAN	COST: $$

HOURS: Sun-Thur, 8AM to 10PM
Fri & Sat, 8AM to 11PM

WHAT TO EXPECT: Live Music • Beach Bar • Cold Beer
Great Views • Watersports Rentals • Super Relaxed

BEST BITES: Mozzarella Sticks • Peel & Eat Shrimp
Rachel Sandwich • Soft Shell Crab Sandwich • Mahi Tacos
The Works Burger • Ultimate Margarita

SCAN FOR MENU

SOME BASICS

Reservations:	NO
Spirits:	FULL BAR
Parking:	LOT
Outdoor Dining:	YES

OPHELIA'S ON THE BAY

9105 Midnight Pass Road
941-349-2212
opheliasonthebay.net

SIESTA KEY	AMERICAN	COST: $$$

HOURS: Dinner Nightly, 5PM to 10PM

WHAT TO EXPECT: Great For A Date • Nice Water View
Good Wine List • Opentable Reservations

BEST BITES: Thai Oishii Shrimp Cocktail • Escargot Ophelia
Vermont Creamery Chevre & Chioggia Beets
Key West Yellowtail Snapper • Thomas Farms Rack Of Lamb

SOME BASICS

SCAN FOR MENU

Reservations:	YES
Spirits:	FULL BAR
Parking:	VALET
Outdoor Dining:	YES

ORIGIN CRAFT BEER & PIZZA CAFÉ

1837 Hillview Street*
941-316-9222
originpizzacafe.com

SOUTHSIDE VILLAGE	PIZZA	COST: $$

HOURS: Sun-Thur, 11AM to 1AM
Fri & Sat, 11AM to 2AM

WHAT TO EXPECT: Neighborhood Feel • Open Late • Friendly Staff
Local Favorite • 4 Sarasota Area Locations • Craft Beer

BEST BITES: Great Wings! • Pizza! • Quinoa Tab'bouleh Salad
Stromboli • Mediterranean Platter • Meatballs

SOME BASICS

SCAN FOR MENU

Reservations:	NO
Spirits:	BEER/WINE
Parking:	LOT/STREET
Outdoor Dining:	YES

OSTERIA 500

1580 Lakefront Drive
941-866-8962
osteria500.com

WATERSIDE PLACE	ITALIAN	COST: $$$

HOURS: Sun-Thur, 11AM to 9:30PM
Fri & Sat, 11AM to 10:30PM

WHAT TO EXPECT: Casual Italian Cuisine • New Waterside Place
No Reservations - First Come, First Served

BEST BITES: Caprese Rivistata • Guazzetto Napoletano
Linguini Cozze E Vongole • Margherita Pizza
Branzino Mediterranero • Profiterole

SCAN FOR MENU

SOME BASICS

Reservations:	NO
Spirits:	FULL BAR
Parking:	LOT
Outdoor Dining:	NO

OSTERIA SOUTHSIDE

1812 South Osprey Avenue
941-361-3200

SOUTHSIDE VILLAGE	ITALIAN	COST: $$

HOURS: Mon-Fri, 9AM to 2:30PM • Sun, 8AM to 2PM
CLOSED SATURDAY

WHAT TO EXPECT: Nightly Specials • Homemade Italian Specialties
Upscale Casual Dining • Great for a Date

BEST BITES: Meatball Salad • Pasta Fagoili • Caprese Salad
Braised Short Rib • Chicken Marsala

MORE INFO

SOME BASICS

Reservations:	NO
Spirits:	FULL BAR
Parking:	STREET
Outdoor Dining:	NO

ORTYGIA

1418 13th Street W.
941-741-8646
ortygiarestaurant.com

BRADENTON	**EUROPEAN**	**COST: $$$**

HOURS: Wed-Sat, 5PM to 8PM
CLOSED SUNDAY, MONDAY & TUESDAY

WHAT TO EXPECT: Intimate Dining Experience • Chef Driven Menu
Nice Outdoor Dining Space • Village Of The Arts

BEST BITES: Mushroom Pate • Veal Piccata • Timballo
"Seafood Of The Week" • Dark Chocolate Pate
Pasta La Norma • Locally Made Gelato

SOME BASICS

SCAN FOR MENU

Reservations:	YES
Spirits:	BEER/WINE
Parking:	STREET
Outdoor Dining:	YES

OWEN'S FISH CAMP

516 Burns Court*
941-951-6936
owensfishcamp.com

BURNS COURT	**SEAFOOD**	**COST: $$**

HOURS: Daily, 4PM to 9PM

WHAT TO EXPECT: Fun Dining Experience • Good For Families
Busy In Season • Parking Can Be A Challenge

BEST BITES: Deviled Eggs • Garlic Snail With Chorizo
Maryland Spiced Shrimp • Low Country Boil
Crispy Chicken • Spicy Jambalaya • Shrimp & Grits

SOME BASICS

SCAN FOR MENU

Reservations:	NO
Spirits:	FULL BAR
Parking:	STREET/LOT
Outdoor Dining:	YES

Patio Salad

The Cottage
Chef Bruno Toso

INGREDIENTS -SALAD
3 cups mixed greens
2 oz candied pecans
½ avocado, sliced
2 oz dried cranberries
2 oz bleu cheese
2 oz super herb tarragon vinaigrette

METHOD - SALAD
Combine ingredients in a large bowl. Toss with Tarragon
Vinaigrette Dressing.

INGREDIENTS - DRESSING
1 cup salad oil
½ cup olive oil
½ cup queen size green olives, chopped
½ cup tarragon vinegar
3 Tbsp Dijon mustard
1½ tsp tarragon
½ tsp basil
½ tsp black pepper
¼ Tabasco
1½ tsp garlic, chopped
3 Tbsp sugar
1½ tsp Worcestershire sauce

METHOD - DRESSING
Mince olives to a super fine consistency in a food processor.

In a large mixing bowl add the processed olives and all of the remaining ingredients. Mix well until of the ingredients are combined. *This will produce more dressing than you'll need for a two person salad. Use as much dressing as you prefer for your salad.*

Located in the heart of Siesta Key Village, The Cottage offers an eclectic dining experience; inspired by the flavors of the world, fresh local seafood, and progressive cooking techniques. Dine al fresco with 2 outdoor dining patios featuring live music every night. We celebrate "Old Florida Charm" with a modern twist.

PACIFIC RIM
1859 Hillview Street
941-330-8071
pacrimsrq.com

SOUTHSIDE VILLAGE	ASIAN	COST: $$

HOURS: Mon-Fri, 11:30AM to 2PM • Mon-Thur, 4:30PM to 9PM
Fri & Sat, 4:30PM to 10PM • Sun, 4:30PM to 9PM

WHAT TO EXPECT: Fun Dining Experience • Sushi & More
Parking Usually Available • Happy Hour

BEST BITES: Crispy Spring Roll • Tuna Carpaccio • Sushi
Sashimi • Drunken Noodles • Wok Dishes • Red Curry
Teriyaki Chicken • Shrimp Tempura • Green Tea Ice Cream

SCAN FOR MENU

SOME BASICS
Reservations:	YES
Spirits:	FULL BAR
Parking:	LOT/STREET
Outdoor Dining:	YES

PALM AVENUE DELI

NEW

1297 North Palm Avenue
941-263-3742
palmavenuedeli.com

DOWNTOWN	DELI	COST: $$

HOURS: Daily, 7AM to 11PM

WHAT TO EXPECT: NY Style Deli • Bustling REAL Deli Feel
QR Table Side Ordering • Palm Ave Garage = Easy Parking

BEST BITES: Matzo Brei • Egg Creams • Burnt Ends Pastrami Hash
Potato Latkes • Palm Avenue Cobb • Matzo Ball Soup
Corned Beef Sandwiches • Stuffed Cabbage • Reuben's

SCAN FOR MENU

SOME BASICS

Reservations:	NO
Spirits:	BEER/WINE
Parking:	STREET/GARAGE
Outdoor Dining:	YES

THE PARROT PATIO BAR & GRILL

3602 Webber Street
941-952-3352
theparrotpatiobar.com

	AMERICAN	COST: $$

HOURS: Sun-Thur, 11:30AM to 11PM
Fri & Sat, 11AM to 12AM

WHAT TO EXPECT: Very Casual • Sports Bar Feel • Live Music
NFL Football Package • Good For Groups

BEST BITES: Smoked Fish Dip • Coconut Shrimp • Buffalo Wings
Buffalo Shrimp • Southwest Taco Salad • Seared Ahi Tuna
Pizza! • Beef On Weck • Grouper Reuben • Burgers

SCAN FOR MENU

SOME BASICS

Reservations:	NO
Spirits:	FULL BAR
Parking:	LOT
Outdoor Dining:	YES

Food Trucks are popular. And, just like every other great food community, we've got our share roaming the streets. Here's a little basic info to help you navigate through the maze of local mobile dining options. These are a few of our favorites!

DOUBLE W RIBEYE WAGON

What They Serve: A delicious ribeye steak sandwich. Also burgers, tacos, and more. Catch one of their Sloppy Joes on special! It will transport you back in time!
Where You Can Find Them: Always parked at 5648 Swift Road. Info at: ribeyewagon.com

HAMLET'S EATERY

What They Serve: Tacos and slider boxes. Both meat and vegan options are available.
Where You Can Find Them:
The Bazaar on Apricot & Lime
Info at: hamletseatery.com

THE MAINE LINE

What They Serve: Lobster a bunch of different ways. Also Clam "Chowdah." Try a Lobstah Grilled Cheese!
Where You Can Find Them: Various locations around the Sarasota area. Check their website for details.
Info at: themaineline.net

SIMPLY GREEK BY WYNNBERRY

What They Serve: Authentic Greek cuisine in a food truck! Gyros, moussaka and more. Try the Greek fries.
Where You Can Find Them:
Various stops around the Sarasota area.
Info at: simplygreekbywynnberry.com

PASTRY ART

1512 Main Street
941-955-7545
pastryartcafe.com

DOWNTOWN	AMERICAN	COST: $$

HOURS: Mon-Sat, 7AM to 4PM
Sun, 8AM to 3PM

WHAT TO EXPECT: Great For A Coffee Date • Wi-Fi
Busy Weekend Spot • Casual Downtown Hangout

BEST BITES: Avocado Toast • Lox & Bagel • Steak & Egg Sandwich
Reuben Sandwich • Beet Salad • Rainbow Salad
Turkey Avocado BLT • Homemade Soup

SCAN FOR MENU

SOME BASICS

Reservations:	NO
Spirits:	BEER/WINE
Parking:	STREET
Outdoor Dining:	YES

PATRICK'S 1481

1481 Main Street
941-955-1481
patricks1481.com

DOWNTOWN	AMERICAN	COST: $$

HOURS: Mon-Thur, 11AM to 9PM • Fri, 11AM to 10PM
Sat, 10AM to 10PM • Sun, 10AM to 9PM

WHAT TO EXPECT: Downtown Since 1985 • Local Favorite
Good Craft Beer Selection • Known For Their Burgers

BEST BITES: Spinach & Artichoke Dip • Roasted Beet Salad
1481 Salad • Award Winning Burgers • Scampi
Fish N Chips • Yankee Pot Roast • Key Lime Pie

SCAN FOR MENU

SOME BASICS

Reservations:	YES
Spirits:	FULL BAR
Parking:	STREET/VALET
Outdoor Dining:	YES

PHILLIPPI CREEK OYSTER BAR

5353 South Tamiami Trail
941-925-4444
creekseafood.com

SOUTH TRAIL	SEAFOOD	COST: $$

HOURS: Daily 11AM to 9:30PM
Happy Hour, 3PM to 5:30PM

WHAT TO EXPECT: Great For Families • Water View • Casual Dining
Busy During Season • Good For Kids

BEST BITES: Oysters Rockefeller • Fried Smelt • Florida Cobb Salad
Jumbo Shrimp Cocktail • Oysters! • "Norfolks"
Steamed Pots • Seafood Paella • Root Beer Float

SOME BASICS

SCAN FOR MENU

Reservations:	NO
Spirits:	FULL BAR
Parking:	LOT
Outdoor Dining:	YES

PHO CALI

1578 Main Street
941-955-2683
phocalisarasota.com

DOWNTOWN	VIETNAMESE	COST: $

HOURS: Mon-Thur, 11AM to 9PM • Fri & Sat, 11AM to 9:30PM
CLOSED SUNDAY

WHAT TO EXPECT: Great Service • Casual Dining
Easy On The Wallet • Good For Families • Noodle Bowls!

BEST BITES: Pork & Shrimp Vietnamese Pancake • Roasted Quail
Daily Specials • Pho Noodle Bowls • Noodle Stir Fry
Rice Vermicelli Noodle Bowls • Roasted Duck

SOME BASICS

SCAN FOR MENU

Reservations:	NO
Spirits:	BEER/WINE
Parking:	STREET
Outdoor Dining:	NO

PICCOLO ITALIAN MARKET & DELI

6518 Gateway Avenue
941-923-2202
piccolomarket.com

GULF GATE	ITALIAN	COST: $

HOURS: Tue-Sat, 11AM to 5PM
CLOSED SUNDAY & MONDAY

WHAT TO EXPECT: Great For A Quick Lunch • Italian Market
Super Casual • Delicious Sandwiches • Catering Available

BEST BITES: Italian Chopped Salad • The Godfather Sandwich
Meatball Parm Sandwich • Pizza! • Pasta Marinara
Chicken Piccata • Cannoli

SCAN FOR MENU

SOME BASICS

Reservations:	NO
Spirits:	NONE
Parking:	LOT
Outdoor Dining:	NO

PIER 22

1200 1st Avenue West
941-748-8087
pier22dining.com

BRADENTON	SEAFOOD	COST: $$$

HOURS: Mon-Thur, 11:30AM to 10PM • Fri, 11:30AM to 10:30PM
Sat, 8AM to 10:30PM • Sun, 8AM to 10PM

WHAT TO EXPECT: Great For A Date • Water View • Good Wine List
Happy Hour • Weekend Brunch

BEST BITES: Asian Lettuce Wrap • Poutine • Fish Tacos
Flatbreads • NE Clam Chowder • Cobb Salad
Grouper Piccata • New York Cheesecake

SCAN FOR MENU

SOME BASICS

Reservations:	YES
Spirits:	FULL BAR
Parking:	LOT
Outdoor Dining:	YES

PIGFISH

5377 McIntosh Road (Calusa Brewing)
941-777-5220
pig.fish

SEAFOOD	COST: $$

HOURS: Tue-Sat, 5M to 9PM
CLOSED SUNDAY & MONDAY

WHAT TO EXPECT: Casual Sustainable Seafood • Calusa Brewing
Redefining The Classic Fish Sandwich • Lots of Parking

BEST BITES: The Pigfish Sandwich • Cobia Hot Dawg • Hush Puppies
Shrimp Fritters • Chicken Katsu • Pork Belly Dawg
Mushroom Grilled Cheese • Chocolate Chip Cookies

SCAN FOR MENU

SOME BASICS

Reservations:	NO
Spirits:	BEER/WINE
Parking:	LOT
Outdoor Dining:	YES

POP'S SUNSET GRILL

112 Circuit Road (ICW Marker 10 by boat)
941-488-3177
popssunsetgrill.com

NOKOMIS	SEAFOOD	COST: $$

HOURS: Daily, 8AM to 10PM

WHAT TO EXPECT: Online "Waitlist" • Serving Breakfast!
Water View • Vacation Atmosphere • Great For Families

BEST BITES: Sunrise Benedict • Shrimp Cocktail • NE Clam Chowder
Pizza! • Raw Bar • Coconut Shrimp • Burgers
Grouper Reuben • Chocolate Toffee Mousse Cake

SCAN FOR MENU

SOME BASICS

Reservations:	NO
Spirits:	FULL BAR
Parking:	LOT
Outdoor Dining:	YES

Grilled Snapper with Roasted Red Pepper Salsa

GROVE Restaurant
Chef Terry Daniels

INGREDIENTS - RED PEPPER SALSA

2 cups roasted red bell pepper, small dice (procedure follows)
1 cup tomato concasse, small dice (procedure follows)
1 TBSP sherry vinegar
1 TBSP honey
1½ tsp extra-virgin olive oil (EVOO)
1 TBSP fresh cilantro (finely chopped)
1 TBSP fresh oregano (finely chopped)
1 tsp salt and pepper
1 tsp fajita seasoning
1/8 tsp Tabasco

METHOD - ROASTED RED PEPPERS

1. Preheat your oven's broiler or grill to high heat.
2. Wash and dry the red bell peppers.
3. Place the whole red bell peppers on a baking sheet or directly on the grill grates.
4. Roast the peppers, turning them occasionally, until the skin is charred and blistered all over (usually about 15-20 minutes).
5. Once charred, transfer the peppers to a bowl, cover it with plastic wrap or a lid, and let them sit for about 10 minutes to loosen the skin with steam.
6. After cooling, peel off the charred skin and remove the seeds and stem.

METHOD - TOMATO CONCASSE

1. Start with ripe tomatoes. Score the bottom of each tomato with an "X."
2. Boil a pot of water and prepare a bowl of ice water.

3. Place the tomatoes in the boiling water for about 30 seconds or until the skin starts to peel back.
4. Quickly transfer the tomatoes to the ice water to cool and stop the cooking process.
5. Peel off the skin starting from the "X" you scored.
6. Cut the peeled tomatoes in half horizontally and remove the seeds and excess liquid.

METHOD - ROASTED RED PEPPER SALSA
Combine all ingredients and season to taste, adding more salt and pepper or Tabasco to adjust to your preference. Store sealed in a container in the refrigerator for up to one week.

GRILLING THE SNAPPER
1. Preheat your grill to medium-high heat (around 400-450°F or 200-230°C).
2. Pat the snapper fillets dry with paper towels and brush both sides with olive oil, ensuring they are well coated.
3. Season the snapper fillets with salt and pepper to taste, adjusting the amount based on your preference.
4. Place the snapper fillets on the preheated grill grates, and you can oil the grates to prevent sticking if needed.
5. Grill the snapper for about 4-5 minutes on each side, or until the fish flakes easily with a fork and has beautiful grill marks. The cooking time can vary depending on the thickness of the fillets.
6. Once done, remove the snapper from the grill and transfer it to a serving platter.
7. Serve your grilled snapper hot, and consider garnishing with lemon wedges for an extra burst of flavor (optional).

Serve with roasted fingerling potatoes and grilled asparagus. This salsa also pairs well with any fish or chicken.

Explore GROVE's Contemporary American cuisine, blending authenticity with imaginative flavors. Enjoy diverse handcrafted dishes, from succulent Pork Osso Bucco to refreshing Seared Ahi Tuna Nachos. Indulge in the cross-cultural twist of our menu, expertly crafted with fresh seasonal ingredients. Experience a memorable dining atmosphere in our inviting spaces – casual patio, spacious dining room, modern bar, and private rooms. GROVE offers a fusion of sophistication and hospitality, ideal for any occasion.

POST KITCHEN & BAR

`NEW`

8433 Cooper Creek Boulevard
941-259-4850
postkitchenandbar.com

COOPER CREEK	AMERICAN	COST: $$$

HOURS: Mon-Thur, 11AM to 9PM • Fri & Sat, 11AM to 10PM
Sunday, 11AM to 8:30PM

WHAT TO EXPECT: Modern American Cuisine • Upscale Atmosphere
Fresh, Local Ingredients • Lots of Parking

BEST BITES: Raw Bar • French Onion Gratine • Tuna Tartare
Lobster Mango Salad • Truffle Pasta • Post Burger
Braised Short Rib • NY Strip Steak • Sticky Ribs

SCAN FOR MENU

SOME BASICS

Reservations:	YES
Spirits:	FULL BAR
Parking:	LOT
Outdoor Dining:	NO

RENDEZ-VOUS FRENCH BAKERY

5336 Clark Road
941-924-1234
rendezvoussarasota.com

	FRENCH	COST: $$

HOURS: Tues-Sat, 7:30AM to 3PM • Sunday, 8AM to 3PM
CLOSED MONDAY

WHAT TO EXPECT: Real French Bakery • Super Casual
The Pastries Are Fantastic! • Catering Available

BEST BITES: La Quiche Lorraine • Le Croque Madame
French Omelettes • French Onion Soup
Baguette Sandwiches • La Nicoise Salad

SCAN FOR MENU

SOME BASICS

Reservations:	NO
Spirits:	NONE
Parking:	LOT
Outdoor Dining:	NO

REYNA'S TAQUERIA

935 North Beneva Road (Sarasota Commons)
941-260-8343
reynastaqueria.com

SARASOTA COMMONS	MEXICAN	COST: $

HOURS: Mon-Sat, 11AM to 9PM
Sun,11AM to 3PM

WHAT TO EXPECT: Family Friendly • Daily Specials
Lots Of Parking • Authentic Mexican Cuisine

BEST BITES: Birria Tacos • Burrito Bowls • Tortas • Sopas
Chips and Guacamole • Churros • Flan

SCAN FOR MENU

SOME BASICS

Reservations:	NO
Spirits:	BEER/WINE
Parking:	LOT
Outdoor Dining:	NO

RICK'S FRENCH BISTRO

2177 Siesta Drive
941-957-0533
ricksfrenchbistro.com

SOUTHGATE	FRENCH	COST: $$$

HOURS: Wed-Sat, 5PM to 9PM
CLOSED SUNDAY, MONDAY & TUESDAY

WHAT TO EXPECT: Initmate Dining Experience • Limited Seating
Authentic French Cuisine • Lots Of Parking

BEST BITES: Soupe a l'Oignon Gratinee • Saumon Fume Sur Toasts
Steak au Poivre • Crevettes a la Marseillaise
Boeuf Bourguignon • Chocolate Mousse

SCAN FOR MENU

SOME BASICS

Reservations:	YES
Spirits:	BEER/WINE
Parking:	LOT
Outdoor Dining:	NO

RIVERHOUSE REEF & GRILL
995 Riverside Drive
941-729-0616
riverhousefl.com

PALMETTO	SEAFOOD	COST: $$$

HOURS: Mon-Thur, 11:30AM to 9PM • Fri, 11:30AM to 10PM
Sat, 11AM to 10PM • Sun, 11AM to 9PM

WHAT TO EXPECT: Waterfront Dining • Happy Hour
Sunday Brunch • Regatta Pointe Marina

BEST BITES: Blue Crab Dip • Oysters • Island Time Salad
Lobster Corn Chowder • Grouper Tacos
Burgers • Lobster Roll • Lobster Pot Pie

SCAN FOR MENU

SOME BASICS

Reservations:	YES
Spirits:	FULL BAR
Parking:	LOT
Outdoor Dining:	YES

ROESSLER'S
2033 Vamo Way
941-966-5688
roesslersrestaurant.com

SOUTH TRAIL	EUROPEAN	COST: $$$

HOURS: Dinner, Tues-Sun, 5PM to close
CLOSED MONDAY

WHAT TO EXPECT: Good Wine List • Private Dining Room
Family Owned & Operated Since 1978 • Online Reservations

BEST BITES: Crispy Duckling New Orleans • Snapper Pontchartrain
Bouillabaisse • Wiener Schnitzel Holstein • Steak Diane
Vichyssois • The Wedge • Bananas Foster

SCAN FOR MENU

SOME BASICS

Reservations:	YES
Spirits:	FULL BAR
Parking:	LOT
Outdoor Dining:	YES

ROSEBUD'S STEAKHOUSE & SEAFOOD

2215 South Tamiami Trail
941-918-8771
rosebudssarasota.com

OSPREY	STEAKHOUSE	COST: $$$

HOURS: Tues-Sun, 4PM to 10PM
CLOSED MONDAY

WHAT TO EXPECT: Early Bird Dining • Private Dining Room
Aged, Hand Cut, Angus Steaks • Established 1995

BEST BITES: Oysters On The Half Shell • Escargot • Duck Wings
Prime Rib • Surf & Turf • Center Cut Pork Chops
BBQ Ribs • Sea Bass "Crab Louie" • Key Lime Pie

SOME BASICS

SCAN FOR MENU

Reservations:	YES
Spirits:	FULL BAR
Parking:	LOT
Outdoor Dining:	NO

THE ROSEMARY

411 North Orange Avenue
941-955-7600
therosemarysarasota.com

ROSEMARY DISTRICT	AMERICAN	COST: $$

HOURS: Tue-Fri, 11AM to 2PM
Sat, 9AM to 2PM

WHAT TO EXPECT: Casual Atmosphere • Busy In Season
Great Outdoor Dining Space • Nice Lunch Spot

BEST BITES: Buttermilk Pancakes • Quiche Lorraine
Omelets • Prix Fixe Lunch Menu • Bermuda Fish Chowder
Thai Chicken Salad • Red Snapper BLT

SOME BASICS

SCAN FOR INFO

Reservations:	YES
Spirits:	BEER/WINE
Parking:	STREET
Outdoor Dining:	YES

BEER
Sarasota's Best

Craft beer, brew pubs, and full on local breweries. Sarasota is not immune to the small batch beer craze. As a matter of fact, we've got some damn good beer craftsmen right here in town. Oh, and along with these local artisans are some great places to down a few unique brews. Here's a list of some of our local favorites. - Cheers!

SARASOTA BREWERIES & BREWPUBS

BIG TOP BREWING
975 Cattlemen Road
Sarasota, FL 34232
941-371-2939
bigtopbrewing.com

BREW LIFE BREWING
5765 South Beneva Road
Sarasota, FL 34233
941-952-3831
brewlifebrewing.com

CALUSA BREWING
5377 McIntosh Road
Sarasota, FL 34233
941-922-8150
calusabrewing.com

FAT POINT BREWING
257 North Cattlemen Road
Sarasota, FL 34243
941-491-2827
fatpoint.com

GOOD LIQUID BREWING
1570 Lakefront Drive
Sarasota, FL 34240
941-238-6466
goodliquidbrewingcompany.com

MOTORWORKS BREWING
1014 9th Street W
Bradenton, FL 34205
941-567-6218
motorworksbrewing.com

SUN KING BREWING
1215 Mango Avenue
Sarasota, FL 34237
941-893-3940
sunkingbrewing.com

SARASOTA BEER BARS

99 BOTTLES
1445 2nd Street
Sarasota, FL 34236
941-487-7874
99bottles.net

SHAMROCK PUB
2257 Ringling Boulevard
Sarasota, FL 34237
941-952-1730
shamrocksarasota.com

Please Drink Responsibly

ROSEMARY AND THYME

511 North Orange Avenue
941-955-7600
therosemarysarasota.com

ROSEMARY DISTRICT	AMERICAN	COST: $$$

HOURS: Tue-Sun, 4:30PM to 9PM
Sunday Brunch, 9AM to 2PM

WHAT TO EXPECT: Upscale, But Casual • Fantastic Sunday Brunch
Great Appetizers • Don't Forget Dessert

BEST BITES: Belgian Waffle • Greek Quiche • Avocado Toast
Bermuda Fish Cake Benedict • Escargots
Pistachio-Dusted Salmon • Steak Frites

SCAN FOR INFO

SOME BASICS

Reservations:	YES
Spirits:	FULL BAR
Parking:	STREET
Outdoor Dining:	NO

SAGE

1216 First Street
941-445-5660
sagesrq.com

DOWNTOWN	AMERICAN	COST: $$$

HOURS: Tues-Thur, 5PM to 10PM
Fri & Sat, 5PM to 11PM

WHAT TO EXPECT: Upscale Dining • Private Event Space
Online Reservations • Rooftop Bar Is Great For A Date

BEST BITES: Seasonal Menu • Bison Short Rib • House Made Rigatoni
Portuguese Mussels • Maple Leak Farms Duck
Beyond S'Mores • Creme Brulee

SCAN FOR MENU

SOME BASICS

Reservations:	YES
Spirits:	FULL BAR
Parking:	LOT/STREET
Outdoor Dining:	YES

SARDINIA

5770 South Tamiami Trail
941-702-8582
sardiniasrq.com

SOUTH TRAIL	ITALIAN	COST: $$$

HOURS: Mon-Sat, 5PM to 10PM
CLOSED SUNDAY

WHAT TO EXPECT: Small & Intimate Dining • Homemade Dishes
Private Dining Room Available • Chef Driven Menu

BEST BITES: Antipasto • Carpaccio • Minestrone • Gnocchi
Lasagna • Ravioli Di Vitello Al Burro, Salvia, Noci E Pecorino
Spigola Al Sale • Chocolate Mousse • Warm Zabaione

SCAN FOR MENU

SOME BASICS

Reservations:	YES
Spirits:	BEER/WINE
Parking:	LOT
Outdoor Dining:	NO

SCHNITZEL KITCHEN

6521 Superior Avenue
941-922-9299
sites.google.com/view/schnitzelsrq/home

GULF GATE	GERMAN	COST: $$

HOURS: Tues-Sun, 4PM to 9PM
CLOSED SUNDAY & MONDAY

WHAT TO EXPECT: Casual Ethnic Cuisine • Homemade Dishes
Big German Beer Selection

BEST BITES: Kinder Sausage • Potato Pancakes • Schweinhaxe
Wiener Schnitzel • Chicken Paprika • Gulash
Schweinebraten • Spätzle • Apple Strudel

SCAN FOR MENU

SOME BASICS

Reservations:	YES
Spirits:	BEER & WINE
Parking:	LOT/STREET
Outdoor Dining:	NO

SCREAMING GOAT TAQUERIA

6566 Gateway Avenue
941-210-3992
screaming-goat.com

GULF GATE	MEXICAN	COST: $

HOURS: Mon-Sat, 11AM to 8PM
CLOSED SUNDAY

WHAT TO EXPECT: Super Casual • Taco Shack • Family Friendly
Great For A Quick Lunch Or Dinner • Private Event Space

BEST BITES: Tacos, Burritos & Bowls • Pork Cochinita Pibil
Latin Falafel • Pollo Asado • Beef Barbacoa
Vegan Chorizo • Chips & Guac

SCAN FOR MENU

SOME BASICS

Reservations:	NO
Spirits:	BEER/WINE
Parking:	LOT/STREET
Outdoor Dining:	NO

SELVA GRILL

1345 Main Street*
941-362-4427
selvagrill.com

DOWNTOWN	PERUVIAN	COST: $$$

HOURS: Sun-Thur, 5PM to 11PM
Fri & Sat, 5PM to 1AM

WHAT TO EXPECT: Great For A Date • Great Ceviche
Late Night & Happy Hour Menus • Also A UTC Location

BEST BITES: Wahoo Ceviche • Selva Wild Ceviche • Tuna Tiradito
Empanadas • Selva's Crab Cake • Atun a la Parilla
Selva's Famous Skirt Steak • Malbec Braised Short Ribs

SCAN FOR MENU

SOME BASICS

Reservations:	YES
Spirits:	FULL BAR
Parking:	STREET/PALM GARAGE
Outdoor Dining:	YES

SHAKESPEARE'S CRAFT BEER & GASTRO PUB

3550 South Osprey Avenue
941-364-5938
shakespearesenglishpub.com

	BRITISH	COST: $$

HOURS: Daily, 11:30AM to 9PM

WHAT TO EXPECT: Great For After Work Meet-Up • Good For Lunch
Fantastic Burger • Traditional English Fare

BEST BITES: Black & Blue Burger • Tomato & Feta Salad
Caramelized Onion & Brie Burger • Cottage Pie
Bangers & Mash • English Fish & Chips

SOME BASICS

SCAN FOR MENU

Reservations:	NO
Spirits:	BEER/WINE
Parking:	LOT
Outdoor Dining:	YES

Scan for the latest Sarasota Restaurant news.
Subscribe to our newsletter

sarasota bites

SHARKY'S ON THE PIER

1600 Harbor Drive South
941-488-1456
sharkysonthepier.com

VENICE	AMERICAN	COST: $$$

HOURS: Sun-Thur, 11:30AM to 10PM
Fri & Sat, 11:30AM to 11PM

WHAT TO EXPECT: Live Music • On The Beach • Very "Florida"
Voted Florida's Best Beach Bar ('13, '18, '19)

BEST BITES: NE Clam Chowder • Cabo Calamari • Sharky's Rice Bowl
Spiced Seafood Nachos • Boathouse Salad
Island Jambalaya • Captain Sharky's Platter

SCAN FOR MENU

SOME BASICS

Reservations:	YES
Spirits:	FULL BAR
Parking:	LOT
Outdoor Dining:	YES

SHEBEEN IRISH PUB & KITCHEN   `NEW`

6641 Midnight Pass Road
941-952-3070

SIESTA KEY	IRISH	COST: $$

HOURS: Tues-Thur, 4PM to 8PM • Fri & Sat, 4PM to 9PM
Sun, 4PM to 8PM • CLOSED MONDAY

WHAT TO EXPECT: Authentic Irish Pub • LIVE Music
Small & Intimate Atmosphere • Grab a Guinness

BEST BITES: Chicken Pot Pie • Corned Beef and Cabbage
Leek & Mushroom Croquettes • Bangers & Mash
Fish & Chips • Shepherd's Pie

SCAN FOR INFO

SOME BASICS

Reservations:	NO
Spirits:	BEER/WINE
Parking:	LOT
Outdoor Dining:	YES

SHORE

465 John Ringling Boulevard*
941-296-0301
dineshore.com

ST. ARMANDS	AMERICAN	COST: $$$

HOURS: Mon-Thur, 11AM to 10PM • Fri & Sat, 11AM to 11PM
Sun, 10AM to 10PM

WHAT TO EXPECT: Online Reservations • Busy During Season
Good Wine List • Happy Hour • Upscale Island Feel

BEST BITES: Tuna Tartare • Diner Meatloaf • Shore Burger
Vegan Kale 'Caesar' • Shrimp & Scallop
Grilled Branzino • Pasta Al Fresco • Thai Curry Mussels

SOME BASICS

SCAN FOR MENU

Reservations:	YES
Spirits:	FULL BAR
Parking:	STREET
Outdoor Dining:	YES

SIEGFRIED'S RESTAURANT

1869 Fruitville Road
941-330-9330
siegfrieds-restaurant.com

DOWNTOWN	GERMAN	COST: $$

HOURS: Wed-Sun, 4PM to 10PM
CLOSED MONDAY & TUESDAY

WHAT TO EXPECT: Casual Dining • Family Owned
Authentic German Cuisine • German Beer-Garden

BEST BITES: Wiener Schnitzel • Sauerbraten
Rheinische Reibekuchen • Leberkase Platter
Spatzle • German Schnitzel

SOME BASICS

SCAN FOR MENU

Reservations:	YES
Spirits:	BEER/WINE
Parking:	LOT/STREET
Outdoor Dining:	YES

Your Pocket Wine
COMPANION

By Lorenzo Muslia, Partner - Andis Wines

Wine is a wonderful world that is hard to simplify into white or red. It is one of the oldest beverages in the world, dating back 5000 years.

In this short list, I have the pleasure of guiding you through a list of wine styles that are easy to find in your local restaurant and wine shop. I prefer to divide wine into five components that are very different from each other:

1) Body can be from light to full, which is how we perceive the wine on our palate.

2) Sweetness can vary from bone dry to sweet and is measured by the residual sugar (RS) found in wine.

3) Tannins is perceived as bitter in wine; the younger the wine is, the more tannins are in it; it also varies from variety to variety. A Pinot Noir has fewer tannins than Petite Sirah.

4) Acidity is what gives the wine a tart and sour taste. It varies from 3.1 for white wines (lemonade is 2.6)pH to just around 4.1 for red wines (coffee is 4.5)pH.

5) Alcohol can taste bitter, sweet, spicy, or oily in different stages. It is formed during fermentation as the yeast converts the sugars into ethanol and releases CO_2. In wine it ranges from 5% to over 15%.

If one of these is very dominant and then we have a wine that is most likely off balance and will not be an easy food pairing, but once these components find a harmonious balance, great pleasure is achieved. Wines that are balanced between their components are easier to pair with food and provide a better taste.

REDS

Red wine is the largest selection of wine on the market, and here's a guide to the most famous varieties and their blends.

CABERNET SAUVIGNON, BORDEAUX BLEND, MERITAGE & BOLGHERI

Characteristics: Black Cherry, White Pepper, Cedar, Graphite, and Baking Spices

Regions: Napa, Sonoma, Bordeaux in France, Bolgheri in Italy

Cabernet Sauvignon is originally from France and is one of the most planted grape varieties in the world today. Its genesis starts as a cross between Cabernet Franc and Sauvignon Blanc. It is known for making full-body wines defined by big and robust tannins, usually wines that can age for several decades. These pair with grilled meats and rich, peppery sauces.

Suggested: Silver Oak Cabernet Sauvignon, Andis Cabernet Franc, or a Bordeaux Blend from the left bank

Other Grapes To Try: Merlot, Carmenere, Cabernet Franc, and Malbec

PINOT NOIR

Characteristics: Cherry, Raspberry, Mushroom, and Vanilla

Regions: Burgundy in France, Oregon, Marlborough in New Zealand

Pinot Noir is the most popular light-bodied red wine. Pinot Noir is a thin-skinned grape variety with moderate to high acidity, low to average levels of soft tannins, and is paler in color than most other red wines.

A red wine made from Pinot Noir has an aroma of red berries and cherry. Many of the more complex examples show hints of the forest floor.

An easy wine to pair with various types of cuisine, such as duck, chicken, and mushrooms.

Suggested: Nuits-St.-Georges 1er Cru "Clos des Porrets St. Georges," Henri Gouges, Sojourn Pinot Noir

Other Grapes To Try: Barbera d'Amador from Andis Wines, Grenache, Nerello Mascalase from Sicily, Gamay

SANGIOVESE & NEBBIOLO

Characteristics: Cherry, Rose, Leather, Espresso, and Oregano

Regions: Chianti, Montalcino, Montepulciano, Scansano for Sangiovese. Langhe, Barolo, Barbaresoc, Valtellina for Nebbiolo

Italy's most famous and acclaimed wines are made from these two grape varieties, Sangiovese and Nebbiolo. Sangiovese is the main grape grown in Tuscany and is responsible for making some of the best wines in the region. Chianti Classico, Brunello di Montalcino, and Nobile di Montepulciano are made using Sangiovese grape. Sangiovese wines are sensitive, balanced, and food friendly.

On the other hand, Barolo and Barbaresco are made from Nebbiolo grapes grown in Piedmont. These two regions deliver a Nebbiolo with delicate aromas and robust tannins age-worthy for up to 50 years.

Typical plates to pair with Sangiovese are tomato based dishes and well-spiced. Nebiolo tastes best with creamy cheese dishes and truffle notes.

Suggested: Brunello di Montalcino Uccelliera, Rosso Di Montepulciano, Barolo Domenico Clerico, Nebbiolo Langhe

Other Grapes To Try: Tempranillo, Aglianico, Xinomavro

ZINFANDEL, SYRAH, GSM BLEND & PETITE SIRAH

Characteristics: Blackberry, Strawberry, Sweet Tobacco, Plum, and Green Peppercorn

Regions: Lodi, Dry Creek, Sierra Foothills for Zinfandel. Passo Robles, North and South Rhone in France For Syrah and GSM, Napa Valley, Paso Robles, Amador County for Petite Sirah

Zinfandel is one of the oldest varieties grown in California. It makes fruit-forward yet bold wines with jammy fruit, smoky, exotic spices, and a hint of pepper. Originally from Croatia, it was made popular in Puglia as Primitivo and is now a California Classic. Zinfandel is ideal for BBQ, Mediterranean dishes, or a juicy burger.

Syrah and GSM blends are rich and powerful wines, sometimes meaty. GSM is a blend of Grenache, Syrah and Mourvedre. These grapes are typically grown in the Rhone region of France but are also very popular in the "new world," such as Australia and California. Darker meats and spices bring out the best notes of Syrah and GSM blends.

Petite Sirah is loved for its dark-colored wines with rich texture and robust tannins. These are wines that are considered full body style. Petite Sirah is related to Syrah but makes a completely different style of wine. The best dishes to pair are fat and umami, steaks from the grill, and beef stroganoff.

Suggested: Painted Fields Old Vine Zinfandel Sierra Foothills, Tablas Creek Cotes Tables Red, Stags Leap Petite Sirah, Gigondas "Le Claux" Chateau Saint Cosme

Other Grapes To Try: Tannat, Sagrantino, Frappato, and Carignan

WHITES

White wine is my favorite category to drink. As a Winemaker and a winery owner, we value each other's jobs based on how good the white wines we produce are. It is an unappreciated category, considering how much attention we devote to producing delicious wines in a third of the time it takes to make red wine.

CHARDONNAY, VIOGNIER & RHONE GRAPES (GRENACHE BLANC, ROUSSANNE, MARSANNE)

Characteristics: Butter, Vanilla, Yellow Apple, Toast, Lemon Zest, Peach, Mango

Regions: Napa, Sonoma, and Santa Barbara in California, Burgundy in France, and Western Australia

Chardonnay is the world's most popular grape. This category of white wines is one of the most consumed in the market. These wines usually are aged in barrels to create a rich and oily, mostly buttery sensation on the palate. They are very complex wines to pair with food, considering their one-note flavor, BUTTER, They are great wines to have on their own, especially if you like semi-sweet wines.

Great food to pair with these wines is buttery and soft, like Lobster, Thai, or Vietnamese cuisine.

Suggested: Rombauer Chardonnay, Far Niente Chardonnay, Puligny-Montrachet, Bouchard Aîné

Other Grapes To Try: Andis Wines Semillon Bill Dillian Vineyard, Chablis, Rioja White Wine

SAUVIGNON BLANC, CHENIN BLANC, VERMENTINO & WHITE BORDEAUX BLEND

Characteristics: Gooseberry, Grapefruit, White Peach, Honey, Pear, Salt, Lemon

Regions: Loire Valley, Napa, New Zeland for Sauvignon Blanc. South Africa and Loire Valley for Chenin Blanc. Sadinia, Bolgheri for Vermentino Bordeaux for white bordeaux blends

This group of wines is known for their herbaceous flavors, low alcohol, perfume notes, and high acidity, making them the perfect sipper on hot summer days. Sauvignon Blanc is a white-wine grape from France, successfully grown in emerging and established wine regions worldwide. The variety produces lightly colored, dry white wines with fresh acidity.

Chenin Blanc, like Sauvignon Blanc, is originally from the western part of France, Loire Valley, and makes fantastic, dry summer whites and sparkling wines. It also offers oak-aged styles with flavors similar to Chardonnay.

Vermentino is a white wine grape grown in various

locations around the western Mediterranean. White wines are often light to medium-bodied, with flavor profiles similar to Sauvignon Blancs; they range from fresh and light-bodied white wines to rich, textural ones depending on their style!

White Bordeaux blends are wines blended from Sauvignon Blanc, Semillon, and Muscadelle. Sauvignon brings grassy aromas to this blend, while Semillon adds a touch of complexity and a waxy, honeyed note. Muscadelle contributes grapey aromas.

Classic white Bordeaux blends are pale gold, with flashes of golden green, characterized by citrus, grass, and hay scents.

These wines pair well with grilled fish, mussels, and oysters.

Suggested: Antrinori Vermentino di Bolgheri, Sancerre "Les Terres Blanches," Domaine Gueneau, Ferrari-Carano Sauvignon Blanc, Vouvray Reserve du Naufraget Chenin Blanc

Other Grapes To Try: Albarino, Greco di Tufo, Picpoul, Vinho Verde

RIESLING & PINOT GRIGIO (PINOT GRIS)

Characteristics: Lime, Green Apple, Jasmine, Raw Almond, Lemon Zest

Regions: Mosel in Germany, Alsace in France, Washington, South Australia, and New York for Riesling. Friuli, Venice, Trentino Alto Adige in Italy, Oregon, Alsace in France, Australia

Riesling and Pinot Grigio are two of the world's oldest

grape varieties, and they are grown in very similar climates. Riesling and Pinot Grigio are medium-bodied white wines. Both wines are usually quite dry, but their fruitiness can trick the tongue into thinking they're a bit sweeter than reality.

Riesling is an aromatic white wine originally from Germany. White wines from Riesling vary in style, from off-dry to sweet wines. They pair very well with spices and Asian cuisine.

Pinot Gris, a.k.a Pinot Grigio, is a pink grape mutation from Pinot Noir, originally from France, but the North Italian style is very popular worldwide. Pinot Grigio makes an excellent pairing with white meats and seafood, or a great glass of wine as a happy hour.

Suggested: Kabinett "Ayler Kupp" Bischofliche Weinguter Trier, Petor Nicolay, Livio Felluga Pinot Grigio Colli Orientali del Friuli, Pinot Gris Ponzi Vineyards

Other Grapes To Try: Albarino, Friulano, Pinot Blanc, Muller Thurgau, Furmit

ROSÉS

Rosé is a type of wine that uses a fraction of a grape's skin color during production, making it different from red wines that use all the pigments. Rosé wines can are made from numerous different types of grapes. The rosé wine category has exploded in the last decade, from being a summer wine to now being an all-year-long presence in almost every restaurant menu worldwide.

LIGHT TO MEDIUM BODY ROSÉ

Characteristics: Grapefruit, Strawberry, Cherry, Rose

This category of Rosé wine is one of the most popular worldwide. They are usually made from thin skin varietals such as Pinot Noir, Gamay, Grenache, Mourvedre, or Cinsault. The color range from light pink salmon to just a few shades above it. They are best paired with light dishes and salads, or drunk as an aperitif.

Suggested; Rose from Provence or North Coast Pinot Noir Rosé

MEDIUM BODY TO RICH

Characteristics: Raspberry, hibiscus, berry jam, and white pepper

Rosés from this category are made from thicker skin grapes, Syrah, Tempranillo, Zinfandel, or Cabernet Franc, and usually are darker shades of the rosé, in some cases closer to a light red wine. The texture of these wines is rich and could easily replace a red wine paired with dishes like grilled chicken, pork, or veggies.

Suggested: Rosé from Tavel in Rhone, Dry Zinfandel Rosé, or Syrah Rosé

SPARKLING WINE

Sparkling wines are a synonym for celebration. That long, classy glass called 'flute' filled with wine and tiny little bubbles puts a smile on our faces and energizes our moment. There are many ways to make them, and any grape varietal can be used from any region of the world. The wine can be white, rosé, or red, and the sweetness can range from dry to sweet. Considering that the Sparkling wine category is vast and has so many variations, we will group them into the most popular ones on the market.

CHAMPAGNE & TRADITIONAL METHOD A.K.A MÉTHODE CHAMPENOISE

Characteristics: Citrus, Yellow Apple, Almond, Toast, Cream

The word 'champagne' is often used incorrectly when ordering wine. Most of the time, what we really mean is Sparkling Wine. Champagne is a sparkling wine made from the French region Champagne and is one of the most expensive sparkling wines on the market. The traditional method, a.k.a méthode champenoise, is made the same way as in Champagne but comes from other regions of the world. Most of the time is nonvintage, except for high-quality vintages, which can be white or rose, dry or off-dry, and rarely sweet.

Dlano de Blanc - white grapes only, mostly Chardonnay
Blanc de Noir - white from black grapes, Pinot Noir or Pinot Munier.

PROSECCO

Characteristics: Green Apple, Honeydew, Pera, Cream

It is Italy's most popular sparkling wine and is created by fermenting Glare grapes grown in Veneto and Friuli Venezia Giulia region. The best region known to produce prosecco is called Valdobbiadene. Like Champagne in France, Prosecco wine can only be made in Italy, and it varies in style from dry to sweet, and it can be white or rosé.

CAVA

Characteristics: Quine, Lime Yellow Apple, Chamomile

Regions: Sparkling Wine is made almost everywhere, but only a few regions succeed and make quality wines. Champagne, Loire, Alsace in France; Franciacorta, Valdobiadene, Asti in Italy; Catalonia in Spain

Cava is Spain's most quality sparkling wine and is made similarly to the Champagne method but using indigenous grapes grown in Spain. Also, Cava can be made as white wine or rose wine, and it has three major tiers that define the quality of the wine. Cava, Cava Reserva, and Cava Gran Reserve.

Lorenzo Muslia is the National Sales Manager and Partner of Andis Wines. The Andis winery is located in the rural wine region of Amador County California. You can join their wine club and find more information about the winery at: andiswines.com.

SIESTA KEY OYSTER BAR (SKOB)
5238 Ocean Boulevard
941-346-5443
skob.com

SIESTA KEY	AMERICAN	COST: $$

HOURS: Mon-Thur, 11AM to 11PM • Fri & Sat, 11AM to 12AM
Sun, 9AM to 11PM

WHAT TO EXPECT: Vacation Atmosphere • Live Music Daily
Sunday Brunch • Oyster Happy Hour • Busy In Season

BEST BITES: Tuna Poke Bites • Wings! • Crab Cakes
The SKOB Salad • Seafood Big Boil • Big Boy Mac N Cheese
Chicken N' Waffles • Blackened Grouper Reuben

SCAN FOR MENU

SOME BASICS

Reservations:	NO
Spirits:	FULL BAR
Parking:	LOT/STREET
Outdoor Dining:	YES

SO FRENCH CAFE

NEW

6280 Lockwood Ridge Road
941-388-8936
sofrenchcafe.com

	FRENCH	COST: $$

HOURS: Tues-Sat, 10AM to 5PM
CLOSED SUNDAY & MONDAY

WHAT TO EXPECT: Casual French Fare • Organic Ingredients
Special Event Nights Including Music & Dancing

BEST BITES: Savory & Sweet Crepes (Buckwheat Crepes Available)
Baguette Sandwiches • Smoothies • Blue Cheese Salad
Coffees & Teas

SOME BASICS

SCAN FOR MENU

Reservations:	NO
Spirits:	BEER/WINE
Parking:	LOT
Outdoor Dining:	NO

SPEAKS CLAM BAR

29 North Boulevard of Presidents*
941-232-7633
speaksclambar.com

ST. ARMANDS	SEAFOOD	COST: $$$

HOURS: Mon-Thur, 11AM to 10PM • Fri & Sat, 11AM to11PM
Sun, 12PM to 10PM

WHAT TO EXPECT: Clams! • "Italian" Clam Bar • Upscale But Casual
Gluten Free Menu • Good For Groups

BEST BITES: Raw Bar • Shrimp Arancini • Drunken Pei Mussels
Lobster Bisque • Maine Lobster Roll • Shrimp & Clam Bowl
Lasagna Bolognese • Chicken Marsala

SOME BASICS

SCAN FOR MENU

Reservations:	YES
Spirits:	FULL BAR
Parking:	GARAGE/STREET
Outdoor Dining:	YES

SPEARFISH GRILLE

1265 Old Stickney Point Road
941-349-1971
spearfishgrille.com

SIESTA KEY	SEAFOOD	COST: $$

HOURS: Daily, 11AM to 10PM

WHAT TO EXPECT: Super Casual • Island Feel
Fresh Seafood • Good For Families • Live Music

BEST BITES: Crispy Fried Grouper Cheeks • Tuna Poke
Fresh Gulf Hogfish • Cheesy Gulf Shrimp And Grits
Gulf Shrimp Po-Boy • Cuban Sammy

SCAN FOR MENU

SOME BASICS

Reservations:	NO
Spirits:	FULL BAR
Parking:	LOT/STREET
Outdoor Dining:	YES

SPICE STATION

1438 Boulevard of the Arts
941-343-2894
spicestationsrq.com

DOWNTOWN	THAI/SUSHI	COST: $$

HOURS: Lunch: Mon-Sat, 11AM to 3PM
Dinner: Mon-Sat 4:30PM to 9PM • CLOSED SUNDAY

WHAT TO EXPECT: Casual Asian Cuisine • Quaint And Comfortable
Vegetarian Options • Thai And Sushi • Nice Outdoor Space

BEST BITES: Thai Calamari • Panang Beef • Ginger Pork
Grouper With Ginger • Amazing Chicken
Tom Yum Goong • Duck With Chili & Basil • Sushi

SCAN FOR MENU

SOME BASICS

Reservations:	YES
Spirits:	BEER/WINE
Parking:	LOT/STREET
Outdoor Dining:	YES

SARASOTA SUSHI
YOUR BEST ROLLS ROLL HERE!

Looking for sushi in Sarasota? You're going to have a decision to make. We have some fantastic and creative sushi chefs that call Sarasota their home. We've got 20+ places where you can indulge. Space is limited here, so we have personally curated a list of some of the best places in town (subject to debate, of course). Whether, you're sitting at the bar or at a table with a group of friends, you can't go wrong with any of these places. Oh, just say "OMAKASE" and watch the magic happen...

Azul Steak & Sushi • 1296 First St. • 343-2122
WHAT TO EXPECT: Like the name says... Happy Hour daily. A little something for everyone on this menu.

DaRuMa Japanese Steak House • 5459 Fruitville Rd • 342-6600
WHAT TO EXPECT: Sushi + Teppan tableside cooking. This place is great for groups and big parties. Now open in The Landings.

Drunken Poet Cafe • 1572 Main St. • 955-8404
WHAT TO EXPECT: Sushi + Thai. A large selection of sushi. Downtown location. Also, lots of cooked options to choose from.

Jpan Restaurant • 3800 S. Tamiami Trl. • 954-5726
WHAT TO EXPECT: Always great. Never a miss here. BIG sushi menu. Super creative presentations. Also, across from UTC mall.

Kiyoshi's Sushi • 6550 Gateway Ave. • 924-3781
WHAT TO EXPECT: Nigiri, sashimi, and maki. That's pretty much it. This is a sushi restaurant. Very upscale creations & presentations.

Pacific Rim • 1859 Hillview St. • 330-0218
WHAT TO EXPECT: One of Sarasota's most established sushi restaurants. Good for groups. Lots of cooked dishes too.

Star Thai & Sushi • 240 Avenida Madera • 217-6758
WHAT TO EXPECT: Really creative & well-presented sushi dishes. Lots of Thai choices as well. Friendly Siesta Key atmosphere.

STAR THAI AND SUSHI
240 Avenida Madera*
941-217-6758
starthaisushisiestakey.com

SIESTA KEY	ASIAN	COST: $$

HOURS: Wed-Mon, 12PM to 11PM
CLOSED TUESDAY

WHAT TO EXPECT: Sushi • Siesta Village • Very Friendly Staff
Live Music • Great For A Date

BEST BITES: Roasted Duck Noodle Soup • Sushi • Panang Curry
Crab Rangoon • Larb Gai • Tom Yum
Pad Thai • Soft Shell Crab • Three Buddies

SCAN FOR MENU

SOME BASICS
Reservations:	YES
Spirits:	FULL BAR
Parking:	STREET/LOT
Outdoor Dining:	YES

STATE STREET EATING HOUSE
1533 State Street
941-951-1533
statestreetsrq.com

DOWNTOWN	AMERICAN	COST: $$

HOURS: Tues-Fri, 5:30M to 11PM
Brunch: Sat & Sun, 10:30AM to 2:30PM

WHAT TO EXPECT: Great For A Date • Comfort Food • Good Wine List
Adult Lounge Scene • Excellent Cocktails

BEST BITES: Red Curry Mussels • Blistered Shishito Peppers
Pork Ragu • Prime Flat Iron Steak • Fried Chicken
State Street Burger • Hand Cut Garlic Parm Fries

SCAN FOR MENU

SOME BASICS
Reservations:	YES
Spirits:	FULL BAR
Parking:	STREET/GARAGE
Outdoor Dining:	YES

STATION 400

400 Lemon Avenue*
941-906-1400
station400.com

ROSEMARY DISTRICT	AMERICAN	COST: $$

HOURS: Daily, 7:30AM to 2:30PM

WHAT TO EXPECT: Great For Lunch Meet-Up • Lots Of Pancakes
Soups, Salads, & Sandwiches • Catering

BEST BITES: Bacon & Salted Caramel Pancakes • Nutella Waffle
Truffle Eggs Benedict • Greek Omelet • Reuben
Cobb Salad • Pressed French Dip • Falafel Wrap

SOME BASICS

SCAN FOR MENU

Reservations:	NO
Spirits:	BEER/WINE
Parking:	LOT
Outdoor Dining:	YES

STIKS

4413 South Tamiami Trail
941-923-2742
stiksfoods.com

SOUTH TRAIL	ASIAN	COST: $$

HOURS: Tue-Thur, 11:30AM to 8PM • Fri & Sun, 11:30AM to 8:30PM
CLOSED MONDAY

WHAT TO EXPECT: Fast Casual Asian Cuisine • Boba!
Lots Of Vegan Options • Great For A Quick Lunch

BEST BITES: Pad Thai • Shiitake Wide Noodles • Green Curry
Lao Curry Noodle Soup • Pho Beef Broth •
Fried Chicken Bites • Rangoons • Pork Dumplings

SOME BASICS

SCAN FOR MENU

Reservations:	NO
Spirits:	FULL BAR
Parking:	LOT
Outdoor Dining:	NO

STOTTLEMEYER'S SMOKEHOUSE
19 East Road
941-312-5969
stottlemyerssmokehouse.com

	BBQ	COST: $$

HOURS: Mon-Wed, 11:30AM to 8PM • Thur, 11:30AM to 9PM
Fri & Sat, 11:30PM to 10PM • Sun, 11:30AM to 9PM

WHAT TO EXPECT: Good For Families • Easy On The Wallet
Live Music • Casual Florida Dining Experience

BEST BITES: Fried Green Tomatoes • Smokehouse Salad
Beef Brisket • Famous Fried Chicken • Pulled Pork
Smoked Sausage Sandwich • Cuban Sandwich

SCAN FOR MENU

SOME BASICS
Reservations:	YES
Spirits:	FULL BAR
Parking:	LOT
Outdoor Dining:	YES

SUMMER HOUSE STEAK & SEAFOOD
149 Avenida Messina
941-260-2675
summerhousesiestakey.com

SIESTA KEY	STEAKHOUSE	COST: $$$

HOURS: Sun-Thur, 4PM to 10PM
Fri & Sat, 4PM to 11PM

WHAT TO EXPECT: Always Busy • Happy Hour • Upscale Dining
Fantastic Service • Excellent Wine List

BEST BITES: Colossal Shrimp Cocktail • Lobscargot
Lobster Bisque • 18oz Bone-In Rib Eye • Diver Scallops
16oz Pork Tomahawk • Pinot Noir Braised Short Rib

SCAN FOR MENU

SOME BASICS
Reservations:	YES
Spirits:	FULL BAR
Parking:	STREET/VALET
Outdoor Dining:	YES

SUN GARDEN CAFÉ

210 Avenida Madera
941-346-7170
sungardencafe.com

SIESTA KEY	AMERICAN	COST: $$

HOURS: Daily, 7:30AM to 1:30PM

WHAT TO EXPECT: Casual Island Lunch • Nice Outdoor Seating
Sandwich/Soup/Salad Combos

BEST BITES: Charleston Grits • Bikini Bagel • Garden Omelets
Shrimp Benedict • Adluh Mills Pancakes • Paninis
Curried Chicken Soup • Southern Fried Salad

SOME BASICS

SCAN FOR MENU

Reservations:	NO
Spirits:	BEER/WINE
Parking:	STREET
Outdoor Dining:	YES

TAMIAMI TAP

711 South Osprey Avenue
941-500-3182
tamiamitap.com

LAUREL PARK	AMERICAN	COST: $$

HOURS: Tue-Sat, 4PM to 2AM • Sunday Brunch, 11AM to 3PM
CLOSED MONDAY

WHAT TO EXPECT: Casual & Fun! • Thursday Open Mic Night
Live Music • Nice Outdoor Dining Space

BEST BITES: Sliders • Hummus • Calamari Fries • Wings
Laurel Park Salad • Impossible Tacos • Shrimp Tacos
Steak Frites • Lobster Roll • Key Lime Pie

SOME BASICS

SCAN FOR MENU

Reservations:	NO
Spirits:	FULL BAR
Parking:	LOT
Outdoor Dining:	YES

TANDOOR

8453 Cooper Creek Boulevard
941-926-3077
tandoorsarasota.net

LWR	INDIAN	COST: $$

HOURS: Lunch: Tue-Sun, 11:30PM to 2:30PM
Dinner: Tue-Sun, 5PM to 9PM • CLOSED MONDAY

WHAT TO EXPECT: Upscale Atmosphere • Serving Since 2001
Authentic Traditional Indian Cuisine • Lots Of Parking

BEST BITES: Aloo Tikki • Paneer Pakora • Tikka Masala
Madras Curry • Chicken Makhani • Channa Masala
Aloo Saag • Chicken Biryani • Chicken Tandoori

SCAN FOR MENU

SOME BASICS
Reservations:	YES
Spirits:	FULL BAR
Parking:	LOT
Outdoor Dining:	NO

TOASTED MANGO CAFÉ

430 North Tamiami Trail*
941-388-7728
toastedmangocafe.com

NORTH TRAIL	AMERICAN	COST: $$

HOURS: Daily, 7:30AM to 2:30PM

WHAT TO EXPECT: Good For Families • Casual Dining • Great Service
Lots Of Menu Choices • Busy On Weekends

BEST BITES: Avocado Toast • Eggs Benedict • Biscuits And Gravy
Waffle N' Egg • Egg Salad Sandwich • Cobb Salad
The Debbie Sandwich • Smoked Salmon Platter

SCAN FOR MENU

SOME BASICS
Reservations:	NO
Spirits:	BEER/WINE
Parking:	LOT
Outdoor Dining:	NO

TOASTIQUE

10 South Lemon Avenue
941-312-4099
toastique.com

NEW

DOWNTOWN	AMERICAN	COST: $$

HOURS: Daily, 7AM to 5PM

WHAT TO EXPECT: Great for a Quick Lunch
Good Lunch Time Meet Up Spot • Light & Bright Atmosphere

BEST BITES: Avocado Smash • Smoked Salmon • Greek
Spicy Crab • PB & B Bowl • Black Mystique Bowl
Purple Heart Smoothie • Cold Pressed Juices

SOME BASICS

SCAN FOR MENU

Reservations:	NO
Spirits:	NONE
Parking:	STREET/GARAGE
Outdoor Dining:	NO

TONY'S CHICAGO BEEF

6569 Superior Avenue*
941-922-7979
tonyschicagobeef.com

GULF GATE	AMERICAN	COST: $

HOURS: Mon-Sat, 11AM to 9PM
CLOSED SUNDAY

WHAT TO EXPECT: Great For Lunch • Easy On The Wallet
Chicago Style Food • Counter And Table Seating

BEST BITES: Chicago Dog • Italian Beef Sandwich • Chicago Brat
Char-Grilled Burgers • Pork Chop Sandwich
Maxwell Street Polish Sausage • Pizza Puffs

SOME BASICS

SCAN FOR MENU

Reservations:	NO
Spirits:	BEER/WINE
Parking:	LOT/STREET
Outdoor Dining:	YES

TRIPLETAIL SEAFOOD & SPIRITS
4870 South Tamiami Trail
941-529-0555
tripletailsrq.com

THE LANDINGS	SEAFOOD	COST: $$$

HOURS: Sun-Thur, 3PM to 9PM
Fri & Sat, 3PM to 10PM

WHAT TO EXPECT: Upscale, Casual Seafood • Happy Hour
Busy In Season • Handcrafted Cocktails

BEST BITES: Street Tacos • Lobster Mac & Cheese • Grouper Bites
Smoked Fish Dip • Fishcamp Chowder • Oysters
Tripletail • Crab Cakes • Ribeye Steak • Lobster Roll

SCAN FOR MENU

SOME BASICS
Reservations:	YES
Spirits:	FULL BAR
Parking:	LOT
Outdoor Dining:	YES

TURMERIC INDIAN BAR & GRILL
1001 Cocoanut Avenue
941-212-2622
turmericsarasota.com

ROSEMARY DIST	INDIAN	COST: $$$

HOURS: Mon, Wed, Thur, Sun, 11AM to 10PM
Fri & Sat, 11AM to 11PM • CLOSED TUESDAY

WHAT TO EXPECT: Indian "Fusion" Cuisine • Private Dining
Event Catering • Upscale Dining Atmosphere

BEST BITES: Dahi Aloo Puri • Lamb Boti Kebab • Momos
Chicken Tikka • Butter Chicken • Chana Masala
Dosa Stuffed • Biryani • Stuffed Naan

SCAN FOR MENU

SOME BASICS
Reservations:	YES
Spirits:	FULL BAR
Parking:	STREET
Outdoor Dining:	YES

TURTLES ON LITTLE SARASOTA BAY

8875 Midnight Pass Road
941-346-2207
turtlesrestaurant.com

SIESTA KEY	AMERICAN	COST: $$

HOURS: Mon-Sat, 11:30AM to 9PM
Sun, 10AM to 9PM

WHAT TO EXPECT: Right On The Water • Old Style Florida Dining
Sunday Brunch • Happy Hour Specials • Since 1986

BEST BITES: Coconut Shrimp • Turtles Wedge • NE Clam Chowder
Grouper Sandwich • Stuffed Shrimp • Fisherman Platter
Coconut Crusted Mahi Mahi • Turtle Pie

SOME BASICS

SCAN FOR MENU

Reservations:	YES
Spirits:	FULL BAR
Parking:	LOT
Outdoor Dining:	YES

EXPERIENCE A SARASOTA FOOD TOUR

KEY CULINARY TOURS

WHAT TO EXPECT: Culinary walking tours of neighborhoods in
Sarasota, St. Armands, Anna Maria island and Venice. Lunch
and dinner tours. A great opportunity to sample local foods; meet
restaurateurs, discover Sarasota neighborhoods, and meet new
friends! They're Sarasota's original culinary touring company.
MORE INFO: keyculinarytours.com or 941-893-4664

TASTE MAGAZINE PROGRESSIVE DINNERS

WHAT TO EXPECT: Remember the neighborhood progressive
dinner? This your chance to experience an upgraded version of
the classic food adventure. *Taste Magazine* sponsors themed
progressive dinners about once every six weeks starting in
December. Their walking historical and food tour of Bradenton
departs every Wednesday & Thursday at 12PM. That's a fun way
to spend a Florida afternoon.
MORE INFO: tasteweb.net or 941-366-7950

TZEVA

1255 North Palm Avenue (Art Ovation Hotel)
941-316-0808
tzevasarasota.com

DOWNTOWN	MEDITERRANEAN	COST: $$

HOURS: Daily - Breakfast, Lunch, and Dinner

WHAT TO EXPECT: Modern Mediterranean Cuisine • Special Events
1st Floor - Art Ovation Hotel • Good For Groups

BEST BITES: Shakshuka • Crab Benny • Greek Omelet
Israeli Salad • Lamb Loin Shashlik • Falafel
Toasted Feta Cheese • Black Sesame Brulée

SCAN FOR MENU

SOME BASICS

Reservations:	YES
Spirits:	FULL BAR
Parking:	GARAGE
Outdoor Dining:	YES

VACCI PIZZA + CUCINA

4406 53rd Avenue E
941-405-4131
vaccipizza.com

BRADENTON	ITALIAN	COST: $$

HOURS: Mon-Sat, 11AM to 9PM
CLOSED SUNDAY

WHAT TO EXPECT: The Valentino's Restaurant Family
Brick Oven Pizza! • Good For Families • Lunch Specials

BEST BITES: Sicilian Arancini • Garlic Knots • Pasta Fagioli
Toni Salad • Margherita Pizza • Roni-Cini Pizza
Nonna's Gravy • Italian Hero • Classic Parm

SCAN FOR MENU

SOME BASICS

Reservations:	NO
Spirits:	NONE
Parking:	LOT
Outdoor Dining:	YES

VENEZIA

373 St Armands Circle
941-388-1400
venezia-1966.com

ST ARMANDS	ITALIAN	COST: $$

HOURS: Daily, 11PM to 10PM

WHAT TO EXPECT: Upscale Italian Bistro • Sidewalk Cafe Dining
No Reservations • Great For A Lunch Meetup

BEST BITES: Mussels Sautéed • Caprese Napoli • Calamari
Meatball Parmigiana • Gnocchi Alfredo
Grouper Francese • Pizza! • Salmon Ele

SOME BASICS

SCAN FOR MENU

Reservations:	NO
Spirits:	BEER/WINE
Parking:	STREET/GARAGE
Outdoor Dining:	YES

VERNONA

NEW

711 Manatee Avenue E
941-284-0416
vernonagourmet.com

BRADENTON	HUNGARIAN	COST: $$

HOURS: Mon-Sat, 7:30AM to 9PM (Closed from 2:30 to 5:30)
Sunday, 7:30PM to 2:30PM

WHAT TO EXPECT: Authentic Hungarian Cuisine • Catering Available
Special Events • Bradenton Riverwalk

BEST BITES: Hortobagyi Palacsinta • Chicken Paprikas
Rantott Sajt • Chicken Schnitzel • Rákóczi Túrós
Meatloaf Hadik Style • Csülkös Strapacska

SOME BASICS

SCAN FOR MENU

Reservations:	YES
Spirits:	BEER/WINE
Parking:	STREET
Outdoor Dining:	NO

VERONICA FISH & OYSTER

1830 South Osprey Avenue
941-366-1342
veronicafishandoyster.com

SOUTHSIDE VILLAGE	SEAFOOD	COST: $$$

HOURS: Mon-Thur, 5PM to 9PM • Fri & Sat, 5PM to 10PM
CLOSED SUNDAY

WHAT TO EXPECT: Busy, Lively Dining Room • Handmade Cocktails
Raw Bar • Upscale Dining • Happy Hour

BEST BITES: Grilled Octopus • Bibb Salad • Smoked Fish Dip
Lobster Fra Diavolo • Pork Belly • Fresh Catch
Thai Crispy Whole Snapper • Blackened Mahi BLT

SCAN FOR MENU

SOME BASICS

Reservations:	YES
Spirits:	FULL BAR
Parking:	LOT/STREET
Outdoor Dining:	YES

ABOUT US

Way back in April 2002, we started dineSarasota as a way to bring up-to-date restaurant and dining information to Sarasota locals and visitors. Our annual printed dining guides and our website, dineSarasota.com, have grown right along with the ever-expanding Sarasota dining scene. Whether you're just visiting or you're a native, we're here to help you make the most of your local dining experiences.

VILLAGE CAFÉ

5133 Ocean Boulevard
941-349-2822
villagecafeonsiesta.com

SIESTA KEY	AMERICAN	COST: $$

HOURS: Daily, 7:30AM to 2PM

WHAT TO EXPECT: Family Owned • Dog Friendly Outdoor Dining
Casual Dining • Open Since 1995 • Good For Families

BEST BITES: Belgian Waffles • Cinnamon Roll French Toast
The Works Omelet • Avocado Toast • Lox & Bagel
Burgers • Tom's Greek Salad • Daily Specials

SCAN FOR MENU

SOME BASICS

Reservations:	NO
Spirits:	BEER/WINE
Parking:	STREET
Outdoor Dining:	YES

WALT'S FISH MARKET AND RESTAURANT

4144 South Tamiami Trail
941-921-4605
waltsfishmarketrestaurant.com

SOUTH TRAIL	SEAFOOD	COST: $$

HOURS: Mon-Thur, 11AM to 9PM • Sun, 11AM to 10PM
Market, 9AM to 8PM

WHAT TO EXPECT: Restaurant & Market • Live Music • Casual Dining
Busy In Season • Since 1918!

BEST BITES: Stone Crab (in season) • Smoked Fish Spread
Peel & Eat Shrimp • Lobster Bisque • Oysters
Fresh Fish Daily • Off The Hook Oscar • Grouper Bowl

SCAN FOR MENU

SOME BASICS

Reservations:	NO
Spirits:	FULL BAR
Parking:	LOT
Outdoor Dining:	YES

LOCAL FARMERS MARKET INFORMATION

SARASOTA FARMERS MARKET
Lemon Avenue
Downtown Sarasota
Saturdays (Year Round)
7AM to 1PM
Rain or Shine
70+ Vendors
sarasotafarmersmarket.org

DOWNTOWN BRADENTON PUBLIC MARKET
Old Main Street (12 St. W)
Saturdays (October thru May)
9AM to 2PM
realizebradenton.com/about-the-market

SIESTA KEY FARMERS MARKET
Davidson's Plaza (5104 Ocean Boulevard)
Sundays (Year Round)
8AM to 12PM
Rain or Shine
siestakeyfarmersmarket.org

PHILLIPPI FARMHOUSE MARKET
Phillippi Estates Park (5500 South Tamiami Trail)
Wednesdays (October thru April)
9AM to 2PM
50+ Vendors
farmhousemarket.org

VENICE FARMERS MARKET
Venice City Hall (401 West Venice Avenue)
Saturdays (Year Round)
8AM to 12PM
thevenicefarmersmarket.org

WHAT'S IN SEASON?

Our Sarasota area farmer's markets really give locals and visitors a taste of fresh Florida flavor. But, our markets are more than a place just to stock up for the week. They're a place to mingle with friends, enjoy some music, or catch up on the latest neighborhood news!

Now you have a good list of places to buy the freshest locally grown produce. But, what's the best time of year to enjoy Florida's fruits and vegetables? When are they at their peak of freshness? Here's a little help.

WINTER > Bell Pepper • Eggplant • Grapefruit
Strawberries • Squash • Tomatoes • Arugula • Kale
SPRING > Cantaloupe • Guava • Lettuce • Mushrooms
Oranges • Papaya • Radish • Swiss Chard • Strawberries
SUMMER > Avocado • Guava • Mango • Eggplant
Peanuts • Sweet Corn • Watermelon • Snow Peas
FALL > Cucumber • Grapefruit • Mushrooms • Lettuce
Snap Beans • Tangerines • Tomatoes • Peppers

We have super fresh seafood here in Sarasota. You can usually find a plentiful supply of grouper, red snapper, pompano, and mahi at our farmer's markets. Of course, you can always find fresh Gulf shrimp in a variety of sizes.

The most anticipated seafood season runs from October 15th through May 1st. That's stone crab season! You're best off to grab these tasty delights towards the beginning of season when they're the most plentiful.

WICKED CANTINA

1603 North Tamiami Trail*
941-706-2395
wickedcantina.com

NORTH TRAIL	TEX MEX	COST: $$

HOURS: Daily, 11AM to 10PM

WHAT TO EXPECT: Casual Dining • Convenient Before A Show
Busy In Season • Happy Hour Daily

BEST BITES: Bar Taco Trio • Wicked Nachos • Cantina Dip
Cowboy Brisket Bowl • Chicken Tortilla Soup
Enchiladas • Tacos • Fajitas • Quesadillas

SCAN FOR MENU

SOME BASICS

Reservations:	YES
Spirits:	FULL BAR
Parking:	LOT
Outdoor Dining:	NO

WOLFIE'S RASCAL HOUSE NEW

1420 Boulevard of the Arts
941-312-4072
originalwolfies.com

ROSEMARY	DELI	COST: $$

HOURS: Daily, 11AM to Last Call

WHAT TO EXPECT: NY Style Deli • Yes, the Same Wolfie's as Miami
Bustling Atmosphere • Happy Hour • Grab & Go Carry Out

BEST BITES: Smoked Fish • Fresh NY Bagels • Matzo Ball Soup
Broasted Chicken • Brisket • Knish • Reuben Sandwich
Corned Beef & Pastrami Sandwiches • Sol's NY Cheesecake

SCAN FOR MENU

SOME BASICS

Reservations:	NO
Spirits:	FULL BAR
Parking:	STREET
Outdoor Dining:	YES

WORD OF MOUTH

6604 Gateway Avenue
941-925-2400
originalwordofmouth.com

GULF GATE	AMERICAN	COST: $$

HOURS: Daily, 8AM to 2PM

WHAT TO EXPECT: Daily Specials • Casual Dining • Good For Families

BEST BITES: Fresh Baked Muffins • Smoothie Of The Day
Omelets • Frittatas • Eggs Benedict
Curried Egg Salad Sandwich • Classic BLT • Cobb Salad

SOME BASICS

SCAN FOR MENU

Reservations:	NO
Spirits:	BEER/WINE
Parking:	LOT/STREET
Outdoor Dining:	NO

YODER'S RESTAURANT

3434 Bahia Vista Street
941-955-7771
yodersrestaurant.com

PINECRAFT	AMISH	COST: $

HOURS: Mon-Sat, 7AM to 8PM
CLOSED SUNDAY

WHAT TO EXPECT: Great For Families • Easy On The Wallet
Busy In Season • Fantastic Service • Pie!!

BEST BITES: Daily Lunch, Dinner & Soup Specials • Great Sides!
Turkey Manhattan • Yoder's Famous Fried Chicken
Roast Turkey • Traditional BLT • Mom's Meatloaf

SOME BASICS

SCAN FOR MENU

Reservations:	NO
Spirits:	NONE
Parking:	LOT
Outdoor Dining:	NO

YOKOSO RAMEN

3422 Clark Road
941-265-1600
yokosoramen.com

	ASIAN	COST: $$

HOURS: Lunch & Dinner, Wed-Mon
CLOSED TUESDAY

WHAT TO EXPECT: REAL Ramen • Good For Families
Milk Teas • Lots Of Parking

BEST BITES: Gyoza • Shrimp Shumai • Yokoso Steamed Buns
Ramen Menu - Tonkotsu, Curry, Shoyu, Nabeyaki

SCAN FOR MENU

SOME BASICS

Reservations:	NO
Spirits:	NONE
Parking:	LOT
Outdoor Dining:	NO

YUMMY HOUSE

1737 South Tamiami Trail
941-351-1688
yummyhouseflorida.com

SOUTH TRAIL	ASIAN	COST: $$

HOURS: Lunch, Daily, 11AM to 2:30PM
Dinner, Mon-Sat, 5PM to 9:30PM • Sun, 5PM to 9PM

WHAT TO EXPECT: Busy In Season • Lively Atmosphere
Lots Of Parking

BEST BITES: Salt & Pepper Shrimp • Peking Duck • Pot Stickers
Egg Drop Soup • Kung Po Chicken • Spicy XO Beef
Szechuan Style Pork • Clams With Black Bean Sauce

SCAN FOR MENU

SOME BASICS

Reservations:	YES
Spirits:	FULL BAR
Parking:	LOT
Outdoor Dining:	NO

Restaurant Name	Address	Phone #
A Sprig of Thyme	1962 Hillview St	330-8890
Almazonica Cerveceria	4141 S Tamiami Trl	260-5964
Alpine Steakhouse	4520 S Tamiami Trl	922-3797
Ama La Vlta Ristorante	1551 Main St	960-1551
Amore	180 N Lime Ave	383-1111
Andrea's	2085 Siesta Dr	951-9200
Anna Maria Oyster Bar	6696 Cortez Rd	792-0077
Anna Maria Oyster Bar	1525 51st Ave E	721-7773
Anna's Deli	6535 Midnight Pass	348-4888
Apollonia Grill	8235 Cooper Creek	359-4816
Athens Family Rest.	2300 Bee Ridge Rd	706-4121
Atria Bread + Coffee	4120 LWR Blvd	751-1016
Azul Steak & Sushi	1296 First St	343-2122
Baker & Wife	2157 Siesta Dr	960-1765
Bar Hana	1289 N Palm Ave	536-9717
Bavaro's Pizza	27 Fletcher Ave	552-9131
Bay Leaf Indian Cuisine	1092 S Tamiami	244-0310
Beach Bistro	6600 Gulf Dr N	778-6444
Beach House Restaurant	200 Gulf Dr N	779-2222
Bean Coffeehouse	5138 Ocean Blvd	260-6400
Beso	30 S Lemon Ave	279-2999
Bevardi's Salute!	23 N Lemon Ave	365-1020
Big Water Fish Market	6641 Midnight Pass	554-8101
Bijou Garden Café	1287 First St	366-8111
Birdrock Taco Shack	1213 13th Ave W	545-9966
Blu Kouzina	25 N Blvd of Pres	388-2619
Blue Koi	3801 Macintosh Rd	388-7738

Restaurant Name	Address	Phone #
BLVD Cafe	1580 Blvd of the Arts	203-8102
Boca Sarasota	21 S Lemon Ave	256-3565
Bohemios Tapas Bar	3246 Clark Rd	260-9784
The Breakfast House	1817 Fruitville Rd	366-6860
The Breakfast Company	7246 55th Ave E	201-6002
Bonjour French Cafe	5214 Ocean Blvd	346-0600
BrewBurgers Pub	360 Commercial Ct	484-2337
Brick's Smoked Meats	1528 State St	993-1435
Brine Seafood	2250 Gulf Gate Dr	404-5639
Bushido Izayaki	3688 Webber St	217-5635
Buttermilk Handcrafted	5520 Palmer Blvd	487-8949
Café Barbosso	5501 Palmer Crossing	922-7999
Café Epicure	1298 Main St	366-5648
Café Gabbiano	5104 Ocean Blvd	349-1423
Café L'Europe	431 St Armands Cir	388-4415
Cafe Venice	101 W Venice Ave	484-1855
Capo Pazzo	2053 Reynolds St	487-8677
Capt. Curt's Oyster Bar	1200 Old Stickney Pt	349-3885
Caragiulos	69 S Palm Ave	951-0866
Casa Masa	2773 Bee Ridge Rd.	922-8226
Casey Key Fish House	801 Blackburn Pt Rd	966-1901
Cassariano	313 W Venice Ave	786-1000
C'est La Vie!	1553 Main St	906-9575
Cha Cha Coconuts	417 St Armands Cir	388-3300
The Chateau Sarasota	2001 Siesta Dr	706-4093
Chaz 51 Steakhouse	549 US-41 BYP	484-6200
Chianti	3900 Clark Rd	952-3186

Restaurant Name	Address	Phone #
Circo	1435 2nd St	253-0978
Clasico Italian Chophse	1341 Main St	957-0700
The Columbia	411 St Armands Cir	388-3987
Connors Steakhouse	3501 S Tamiami Trl	260-3232
The Cottage	153 Avenida Messina	312-9300
Crab & Fin	420 St Armands Cir	388-3964
The Crow's Nest	1968 Tarpon Ctr Dr	484-9551
Curry Station	3550 Clark Rd	924-7222
Daiquiri Deck Raw Bar	5250 Ocean Blvd	349-8697
Daiquiri Deck Raw Bar	325 John Ringling Blvd	388-3325
Daiquiri Deck Raw Bar	300 W Venice Ave	488-0649
Daiquiri Deck Raw Bar	1250 Stickney Pt Rd	312-2422
DaRuMa Japanese	5459 Fruitville Rd	342-6600
DaRuMa Japanese	4910 S. Tamiami Trl	552-9465
Deep Lagoon Seafood	482 Blackburn Pt Rd	770-3337
Demetrio's Pizzeria	4410 S Tamiami Trl	922-1585
Der Dutchman	3713 Bahia Vista	955-8007
Dim Sum King	8194 Tourist Center Dr	306-5848
Doggystyle	1544 Main St	260-5835
Dolce Italia	6606 Superior Ave	921-7007
Double Deez Hot Dogs	3009 Gulf Dr N	251-5595
Drift Kitchen	700 Benjamin Franklin	388-2161
Drunken Poet Café	1572 Main St	955-8404
Dry Dock Waterfront	412 Gulf of Mexico Dr	383-0102
Dutch Valley Restaurant	6731 S Tamiami Trl	924-1770
Duval's, Fresh, Local...	1435 Main St	312-4001
El Melvin Cocina	1355 Main St	366-1618
El Toro Bravo	3218 Clark Rd	924-0006

Restaurant Name	Address	Phone #
Euphemia Haye	5540 Gulf of Mexico Dr	383-3633
1592 Wood Fired Kitch	1592 Main St	365-2234
481 Gourmet	481 N Orange Ave	362-0400
F.L.A. Deli	2805 Proctor Rd	217-5710
Faicco's Italian Heros	3590 Webber St	960-1395
Fat Point Brewing	257 N Cattlemen Rd	491-2827
Figaro Bistro	1944 Hillview St	960-2109
Fins At Sharky's	1600 Harbor Dr S	999-3467
Flavio's Downtown	1766 Main St	960-2305
Flavio's Siesta Key	5239 Ocean Blvd	349-0995
Florence & Spice Boys	4990 S Tamiami Trl	405-3890
Food + Beer	6528 Superior Ave	952-3361
Fork & Hen	2801 N Tamiami Trl	960-1212
Gecko's Grill & Pub	6606 S Tamiami Trl	248-2020
Gecko's Grill & Pub	5588 Palmer Crossing	923-6061
Gecko's Grill & Pub	351 N Cattlemen Rd	378-0077
Gecko's Grill & Pub	1900 Hillview St	953-2929
Gentile Cheesesteaks	7523 S Tamiami Trl	926-0441
Gilligan's Island Bar	5253 Ocean Blvd	349-4759
Good Liquid Brewing	1570 Lakefront Dr	238-6466
Grandpa's Schnitzel	2700 Stickney Pt Rd	922-3888
The Grasshopper	7253 S Tamiami Trl	923-3688
Graze Street AMI	3218 E Bay Dr	896-6320
GROVE Restaurant	10670 Boardwalk Lp	893-4321
Harry's Continental Kit.	525 St Judes Dr	383-0777
Hob Nob Drive-In	1701 Washington Blvd	955-5001
The Hub Baha Grill	5148 Ocean Blvd	349-6800

Restaurant Name	Address	Phone #
Il Panificio	1703 Main St	366-5570
Il Panificio	215 Avenida Madera	800-5570
Indigenous	239 Links Ave	706-4740
Island House Tap & Grl.	5110 Ocean Blvd	312-9205
Jack Dusty	1111 Ritz-Carlton Dr	309-2266
Jersey Girl Bagels	5275 University Pkwy	388-8910
Joey D's Chicago Style	3811 Kenny Dr.	378-8900
Jpan Sushi & Grill	3800 S Tamiami Trl	954-5726
Jpan Sushi & Grill	229 N Cattlemen Rd	954-5726
JR's Old Packinghouse	987 S Packinghse Rd	371-9358
Ka Papa Cuisine	1830 S Osprey Ave	600-8590
Kiyoski's Sushi	6550 Gateway Ave	924-3781
Knick's Tavern & Grill	1818 S Osprey Ave	955-7761
Kojo	1289 N Palm Ave	536-9717
Kolukan	6644 Gateway Ave	921-3133
Kore Steakhouse	1561 Lakefront Dr	928-5673
Lazy Lobster	5350 Gulf of Mex Dr	388-0440
Libby's Bistro	1917 S Osprey Ave	487-7300
Lila	1576 Main St	296-1042
The Lobster Pot	5157 Ocean Blvd	349-2323
Lobstercraft	28 S Blvd of Pres	346-6325
Lovely Square	6559 Gateway Ave	724-2512
Lynches Pub & Grub	19 N Blvd of Pres	388-5550
The Mable	2831 N Tamiami Trl	487-7373
Made	1990 Main St	953-2900
Mademoiselle Paris	8527 Cooper Creek Bl	355-2323
Mademoiselle Paris	1605 Main St	544-4021

Restaurant Name	Address	Phone #
Madfish Grill	4059 Cattlemen Rd	377-3474
Madison Avenue Deli	28 N Blvd of Pres	388-3354
Main Bar Sandwich Shop	1944 Main St	955-8733
Maison Blanche	2605 Gulf of Mex	383-8088
Malmosto	2085 Siesta Dr	706-1460
Mar-Vista Restaurant	760 Broadway St	383-2391
Marcello's Ristorante	4155 S Tamiami Trl	921-6794
Marina Jack's	2 Marina Plaza	365-4243
Mattison's City Grille	1 N Lemon Ave	330-0440
Mattison's Forty One	7275 S Tamiami Trl	921-3400
Mean Deans Local Kitch	6059 26th St W	251-5435
Mediterraneo	1970 Main St	365-4122
Melange	1568 Main St	953-7111
Meliora	1920 Hillview St	444-7692
Meshugana Deli	4001 Clark Rd	933-0244
Michael John's	1040 Carlton Arms	747-8032
Michael's On East	1212 East Ave	366-0007
Michelle's Brown Bag	1819 Main St	365-5858
Miguel's	6631 Midnight Pass	349-4024
Molly's Pub	1562 Main St	366-7711
Millie's Cafe	3900 Clark Rd	923-4054
Monk's Steamer Bar	6690 Superior Ave	927-3388
Munchies 420 Café	6639 Superior Ave	929-9893
99 Bottles Taproom	1445 2nd St	487-7874
Namo Izakaya	1439 Main St	362-3332
Nancy's Bar-B-Que	14475 SR 70	999-2390
Napule Ristorante	7129 S Tamiami Trl	556-9639

Restaurant Name	Address	Phone #
New Pass Grill	1505 Ken Thompson	388-3050
Oak & Stone	5405 University Pkwy	225-4590
Oak & Stone	4067 Clark Rd	893-4881
Oasis Café	3542 S Osprey Ave	957-1214
The Old Salty Dog	5023 Ocean Blvd	349-0158
The Old Salty Dog	160 Ken Thompson Pk	388-4311
The Old Salty Dog	1485 S Tamiami Trl	483-1000
O'Leary's Tiki Bar	5 Bayfront Dr	953-7505
Ophelia's on the Bay	9105 Midnight Pass	349-2212
Origin Beer & Pizza	3837 Hillview St	316-9222
Origin Beer & Pizza	5070 Clark Rd	217-6533
Origin Beer & Pizza	8193 Tourist Ctr Dr	358-5850
Osteria 500	1580 Lakefront Dr	866-8962
Osteria Southside	1812 S Osprey Ave	361-3200
Owen's Fish Camp	516 Burns Ct	951-6936
Pacific Rim	1859 Hillview St	330-8071
Palm Avenue Deli	1297 N Palm Ave	263-3742
Parrot Patio Bar & Grill	3602 Webber St	952-3352
Pastry Art Bakery	1512 Main St	955-7545
Patrick's 1481	1481 Main St	955-1481
Phillippi Creek Oyster	5363 S Tamiami Trl	925-4444
Pho Cali	1578 Main St	955-2683
Piccolo Italian Market	6518 Gateway Ave	923-2202
Pigfish	5377 McIntosh Rd	777-5220
Pier 22	1200 1st Avenue W	748-8087
Pop's Sunset Grill	112 Circuit Rd	488-3177
Post Kitchen + Bar	8433 Cooper Ck Blvd	259-4850
Rendez-Vous Bakery	5336 Clark Rd	924-1234

Restaurant Name	Address	Phone #
Rendez-Vous Bakery	2117 Siesta Dr	552-9240
Reyna's Taqueria	935 N Beneva Rd	260-8343
Rick's French Bistro	2177 Siesta Dr	957-0533
Riverhouse Reef & Grill	995 Riverside Dr	729-0616
Roessler's	2033 Vamo Way	966-5688
Rosebud's Steakhouse	2215 S Tamiami Trl	918-8771
The Rosemary	411 N Orange Ave	955-7600
Rosemary & Thyme	511 N Orange Ave	955-7600
Sage	1216 1st St	445-5660
Sardinia	5770 S Tamiami Trl	702-8582
Schnitzel Kitchen	6521 Superior Ave	922-9299
Screaming Goat Taq.	6606 Superior Ave	210-3992
Selva Grill	1345 Main St	362-4427
Shakespeare's Eng. Pub	3550 S Osprey Ave	364-5938
Sharky's on the Pier	1600 Harbor Dr S	488-1456
Shebeen Irish Pub	6641 Midnight Pass	952-3070
Shore Diner	465 John Ringling	296-0303
Siegfried's Restaurant	1869 Fruitville Rd	330-9330
Siesta Key Oyster Bar	5238 Ocean Blvd	346-5443
So French Cafe	6280 Lockwood Rdg	388-8936
Speaks Clam Bar	29 N Blvd of Pres.	232-7633
Spearfish Grille	1265 Old Stickney Pt	349-1970
Spice Station	1438 Blvd of the Arts	343-2894
Star Thai & Sushi	240 Avenida Madera	217-6758
State St. Eating House	1533 State St	951-1533
Station 400	400 Lemon Ave	906-1400
Station 400	8215 Lakewood Main	907-0648

Restaurant Name	Address	Phone #
Stiks	4413 S Tamiami Trl	923-2742
Stottlemeyer's Smokehs	19 East Rd	312-5969
The Summer House	149 Avenida Messina	206-2675
Sun Garden Café	210 Avenida Madera	346-7170
Tamiami Tap	711 S Osprey Ave	500-3182
Tandoor	8453 Cooper Creek	926-3070
Toasted Mango Café	430 N Tamiami Trl	388-7728
Toasted Mango Café	6621 Midnight Pass	552-6485
Toastique	10 S Lemon Ave	312-4099
Tommy Bahama Café	300 John Ringling Blvd	388-2888
Tony's Chicago Beef	6569 Superior Ave	922-7979
Tripletail Seafood	4870 S Tamiami Trl	529-0555
Turmeric	1001 Cocoanut Ave	212-2622
Turtle's	8875 Midnight Pass	340-2207
Tzeva	1255 N Palm Ave	413-7425
Vacci Pizza & Cucina	4406 53rd Ave E	405-4131
Venizia	373 St Armands Cir	388-1400
Vernona	711 Manatee Ave E	284-0416
Veronica Fish & Oyster	1830 S Osprey Ave	366-1342
Village Café	5133 Ocean Blvd	349-2822
Walt's Fish Market	4144 S Tamiami Trl	921-4605
Wicked Cantina	1603 N Tamiami Trl	821-2990
Wolfie's Rascal House	1454 Blvd of the Arts	312-4072
Word of Mouth	6604 Gateway Ave	925-2400
Yoder's Restaurant	3434 Bahia Vista	955-7771
Yokoso Ramen	3422 Clark Rd	265-1600
Yume Sushi	1532 Main St	363-0604
Yummy House	1737 S Tamiami Trl	351-1688

AMERICAN		
Restaurant Name	**Address**	**Phone #**
Atria Bread + Coffee	4120 LWR Blvd	751-1016
Baker & Wife	2157 Siesta Dr	960-1765
Beach Bistro	6600 Gulf Dr N	778-6444
Beach House Rest.	200 Gulf Dr N	779-2222
Bean Coffeehouse	5138 Ocean Blvd	260-6400
Bijou Café	1287 First St	366-8111
BLVD Cafe	1580 Blvd of the Arts	203-8102
Boca Sarasota	21 S. Lemon Ave	256-3565
The Breakfast Company	7246 55th Ave E	201-6002
The Breakfast House	1817 Fruitville Rd	366-6860
Brick's Smoked Meats	1528 State St	993-1435
BrewBurgers Pub	360 Commercial Ct	484-2337
Buttermilk Handcrafted	5520 Palmer Blvd	487-8949
Cafe Venice	101 W Venice Ave	484-1855
Cha Cha Coconuts	417 St Armands Cir	388-3300
Clayton's Siesta Grille	1256 Old Stickney Pt	349-2800
The Cottage	153 Avenida Messina	312-9300
Daiquiri Deck Raw Bar	5250 Ocean Blvd	349-8697
Daiquiri Deck Raw Bar	325 John Ringling Blvd	388-3325
Daiquiri Deck Raw Bar	300 W Venice Ave	488-0649
Daiquiri Deck Raw Bar	1250 Stickney Pt Rd	312-2422
Doggystyle	1544 Main St	260-5835
Double Deez Hot Dogs	3009 Gulf Dr N	251-5595
Drift Kitchen	700 Benjamin Franklin	388-2161
Der Dutchman	3713 Bahia Vista	955-8007
Dutch Valley Restaurant	6731 S Tamiami Trl	924-1770

AMERICAN		
Restaurant Name	**Address**	**Phone #**
Duval's, Fresh, Local...	1435 Main St	312-4001
Euphemia Haye	5540 Gulf of Mexico Dr	383-3633
481 Gourmet	481 N Orange Ave	362-0400
Fat Point Brewing	257 N Cattlemen Rd	491-2827
Food + Beer	6528 Superior Ave	952-3361
Fork & Hen	2801 N Tamiami Trl	960-1212
Gecko's Grill & Pub	6606 S Tamiami Trl	248-2020
Gecko's Grill & Pub	1900 Hillview St	953-2929
Gecko's Grill & Pub	5588 Palmer Crossing	923-6061
Gecko's Grill & Pub	351 N Cattlemen Rd	378-0077
Gentile Cheesesteaks	7523 S Tamiami Trl	926-0441
Gilligan's Island Bar	5253 Ocean Blvd	349-4759
Good Liquid Brewing	1570 Lakefront Dr	238-6466
Graze Street AMI	3218 E Bay Dr	890-0020
GROVE Restaurant	10670 Boardwalk Lp	893-4321
Harry's Continental Kit.	525 St Judes Dr	383-0777
Hob Nob Drive-In	1701 Washington Blvd	955-5001
The Hub Baha Grill	5148 Ocean Blvd	349-6800
Indigenous	239 Links Ave	706-4740
Island House Tap & Grl.	5110 Ocean Blvd	312-9205
Jack Dusty	1111 Ritz-Carlton Dr	309-2266
Joey D's Chicago Style	3811 Kenny Dr.	378-8900
JR's Old Packinghouse	987 S Packinghouse	371-9358
Knick's Tavern & Grill	1818 S Osprey Ave	955-7761
Libby's	1917 S Osprey Ave	487-7300
Lovely Square	6559 Gateway Ave	724-2512

AMERICAN		
Restaurant Name	**Address**	**Phone #**
The Mable	2831 N Tamiami Trl	487-7373
Made	1990 Main St	953-2900
Madfish Grill	4059 Cattlemen Rd	377-3474
Marina Jack's	2 Marina Plaza	365-4243
Mattison's City Grille	1 N Lemon Ave	330-0440
Mattison's Forty One	7275 S Tamiami Trl	921-3400
Mean Deans Local Kitch	6059 26th St W	251-5435
Meliora	1920 Hillview St	444-7692
Melange	1568 Main St	953-7111
Michael John's	1040 Carlton Arms	747-8032
Michael's On East	1212 East Ave	366-0007
Millie's Cafe	3900 Clark Rd	923-4054
Munchies 420 Café	6639 Superior Ave	929-9893
99 Bottles Taproom	1445 2nd St	487-7874
Nancy's Bar-B-Que	14475 SR 70	999-2390
New Pass Grill	1505 Ken Thompson	388-3050
Oak & Stone	5405 University Pkwy	225-4590
Oak & Stone	4067 Clark Rd	893-4881
Oasis Cafe	3542 S Osprey Ave	957-1214
The Old Salty Dog	5023 Ocean Blvd	349-0158
The Old Salty Dog	160 Ken Thompson Pk	388-4311
The Old Salty Dog	1485 S Tamiami Trl	483-1000
O'Leary's Tiki Bar	5 Bayfront Dr	953-7505
Ophelia's on the Bay	9105 Midnight Pass	349-2212
Parrot Patio Bar & Grill	3602 Webber St	952-3352
Pastry Art Bakery	1512 Main St	955-7545

AMERICAN		
Restaurant Name	**Address**	**Phone #**
Patrick's 1481	1481 Main St	955-1481
Pigfish	5377 McIntosh Rd	777-5220
Pier 22	1200 1st Avenue W	748-8087
Pop's Sunset Grill	112 Circuit Rd	488-3177
Post Kitchen + Bar	8433 Cooper Ck Blvd	259-4850
The Rosemary	411 N Orange Ave	955-7600
Rosemary & Thyme	511 N Orange Ave	955-7600
Sage	1216 1st St	445-5660
The Sandbar	100 Spring Ave	778-0444
Sharky's on the Pier	1600 Harbor Dr S	488-1456
Shore Diner	465 John Ringling Blvd	296-0303
Siesta Key Oyster Bar	5238 Ocean Blvd	346-5443
State St. Eating House	1533 State St	951-1533
Station 400	400 Lemon Ave	906-1400
Station 400	8215 Lakewood Main	907-0648
Stottlemeyer's Smokehs	19 East Rd	312-5969
Sun Garden Cafe	210 Avenida Madera	346-7170
Tamiami Tap	711 S Osprey Ave	500-3182
Toasted Mango Café	6621 Midnight Pass	552-6485
Toasted Mango Café	430 N Tamiami Trl	388-7728
Toastique	10 S Lemon Ave	312-4099
Tommy Bahama Café	300 John Ringling Blvd	388-2888
Tony's Chicago Beef	6569 Superior Ave	922-7979
Turtle's	8875 Midnight Pass	346-2207
Village Café	5133 Ocean Blvd	349-2822
Word of Mouth	6604 Gateway Ave	925-2400
Yoder's Restaurant	3434 Bahia Vista	955-7771

ASIAN		
Restaurant Name	Address	Phone #
Azul Steak & Sushi	1296 First St	343-2122
Bar Hana	1289 N Palm Ave	536-9717
Blue Koi	3801 Macintosh Rd	388-7738
DaRuMa Japanese	4910 S. Tamiami Trl	552-9465
Dim Sum King	8194 Tourist Center Dr	306-5848
Drunken Poet Café	1572 Main St	955-8404
Jpan Sushi & Grill	3800 S Tamiami Trl	954-5726
Jpan Sushi & Grill	229 N Cattlemen Rd	954-5726
Kiyoski's Sushi	6550 Gateway Ave	924-3781
Kojo	1289 N Palm Ave	536-9717
Kore Steakhouse	1561 Lakefront Dr	928-5673
Namo Izakaya	1439 Main St	362-3332
Pacific Rim	1859 Hillview St	330-8071
Pho Cali	1578 Main St	955-2683
Spice Station	1438 Blvd of the Arts	343-2894
Star Thai & Sushi	240 Avenida Madera	217-6758
Stiks	4413 S Tamiami Trl	923-2742
Yokoso Ramen	3422 Clark Rd	265-1600
Yummy House	1737 S Tamiami Trl	351-1688
CUBAN, MEXICAN & SPANISH		
Beso	30 S Lemon Ave	279-2999
Birdrock Taco Shack	1213 13th Ave W	545-9966
Bohemios Tapas Bar	3246 Clark Rd	260-9784
Casa Masa	2773 Bee Ridge Rd.	922-8226
Circo	1435 2nd St	253-0978

CUBAN, MEXICAN & SPANISH		
Restaurant Name	Address	Phone #
The Columbia	411 St Armands Cir	388-3987
El Melvin Cocina	1355 Main St	366-1618
El Toro Bravo	2720 Stickney Pt Rd	924-0006
The Grasshopper	7253 S Tamiami Trl	923-3688
Kolukan	6644 Gateway Ave	921-3133
Reyna's Taqueria	935 N Beneva Rd	260-8343
Screaming Goat Taq.	6606 Superior Ave	210-3992
Wicked Cantina	1603 N Tamiami Trl	821-2990

DELI		
Anna's Deli	6535 Midnight Pass	348-4888
Faicco's Italian Heros	3590 Webber St	960-1395
Gentile Cheesesteaks	7523 S Tamiami Trl	926-0441
Jersey Girl Bagels	5275 University Pkwy	388-8910
Main Bar Sandwich Shp	1944 Main St	955-8733
Meshugana Deli	4001 Clark Rd	933-0244
Michelle's Brown Bag	1819 Main St	365-5858
Palm Avenue Deli	1297 N Palm Ave	263-3742
Piccolo Italian Market	6518 Gateway Ave	923-2202
Wolfie's Rascal House	1454 Blvd of the Arts	312-4072

ENGLISH, IRISH & SCOTTISH		
Lynches Pub & Grub	19 N Blvd of Pres	388-5550
Molly's Pub	1562 Main St	366-7711
Shakespeare's	3550 S Osprey Ave	364-5938
Shebeen Irish Pub	6641 Midnight Pass	952-3070

FRENCH		
Restaurant Name	**Address**	**Phone #**
A Sprig of Thyme	1962 Hillview St	330-8890
Bonjour French Cafe	5214 Ocean Blvd	346-0600
Rick's French Bistro	2177 Siesta Dr	957-0533
C'est La Vie!	1553 Main St	906-9575
Figaro Bistro	1944 Hillview St	960-2109
Mademoiselle Paris	8527 Cooper Creek Bl	355-2323
Maison Blanche	2605 Gulf of Mexico Dr	383-8088
Miguel's	6631 Midnight Pass	349-4024
So French Cafe	6280 Lockwood Rdg	388-8936

GREEK		
Apollonia Grill	8235 Cooper Creek	359-4816
Athens Family Rest.	2300 Bee Ridge Rd	706-4121
Blu Kouzina	25 N Blvd of Pres	388-2619
1592 Wood Fired Kitch	1592 Main St	365-2234

INDIAN		
Bay Leaf Indian Cuisine	1092 S Tamiami	244-0310
Curry Station	3550 Clark Rd	924-7222
Tandoor	8453 Cooper Creek	926-3070
Turmeric	1001 Cocoanut Ave	212-2622

ITALIAN		
Amore	180 N Lime Ave	383-1111
Andrea's	2085 Siesta Dr	951-9200
Bevardi's Salute!	23 N Lemon Ave	365-1020
Café Barbosso	5501 Palmer Crossing	922-7999
Café Epicure	1298 Main St	366-5648

ITALIAN		
Restaurant Name	**Address**	**Phone #**
Café Gabbiano	5104 Ocean Blvd	349-1423
Café L'Europe	431 St Armands Cir	388-4415
Capo Pazzo	2053 Reynolds St	487-8677
Caragiulos	69 S Palm Ave	951-0866
Cassariano	313 W Venice Ave	786-1000
Chianti	3900 Clark Rd	952-3186
Clasico Italian Chophse	1341 Main St	957-0700
Dolce Italia	6606 Superior Ave	921-7007
Flavio's on Main	1766 Main St	960-2305
Flavio's Brick Oven	5239 Ocean Blvd	349-0995
Malmosto	2085 Siesta Dr	706-1460
Marcello's Ristorante	4155 S Tamiami Trl	921-6794
Mediterraneo	1970 Main St	365-4122
Napule Ristorante	7129 S Tamiami Trl	556-9639
Osteria 500	1580 Lakefront Dr	866-8962
Osteria Southside	1812 S Osprey Ave	361-3200
Piccolo Italian Market	6518 Gateway Ave	923-2202
Sardinia	5770 S Tamiami Trl	702-8582
Vacci Pizza & Cucina	4406 53rd Ave E	405-4131
Venizia	373 St Armands Cir	388-1400

SEAFOOD		
Anna Maria Oyster Bar	6696 Cortez Rd	792-0077
Big Water Fish Market	6641 Midnight Pass	554-8101
Brine Seafood	2250 Gulf Gate Dr	404-5639
Capt. Curt's Oyster Bar	1200 Old Stickney Pt	349-3885
Casey Key Fish House	801 Blackburn Pt Rd	966-1901

SEAFOOD		
Restaurant Name	**Address**	**Phone #**
Crab & Fin	420 St Armands Cir	388-3964
The Crow's Nest	1968 Tarpon Ctr Dr	484-9551
Dry Dock Waterfront	412 Gulf of Mexico Dr	383-0102
Deep Lagoon Seafood	482 Blackburn Pt Rd	770-3337
Duval's, Fresh, Local...	1435 Main St	312-4001
Fins At Sharky's	1600 Harbor Dr S	999-3467
Lazy Lobster	5350 Gulf of Mexico Dr	388-0440
Lobstercraft	28 S Blvd of Pres	346-6325
The Lobster Pot	5157 Ocean Blvd	349-2323
Mar-Vista Restaurant	760 Broadway St	383-2391
Monk's Steamer Bar	6690 Superior Ave	927-3388
Ophelia's on the Bay	9105 Midnight Pass	349-2212
Owen's Fish Camp	516 Burns Ct	951-6936
Phillippi Creek Oyster	5363 S Tamiami Trl	925-4444
Pigfish	5377 McIntosh Rd	777-5220
Siesta Key Oyster Bar	5238 Ocean Blvd	346-5443
Speaks Clam Bar	29 N Blvd of Pres.	232-7633
Spearfish Grille	1265 Old Stickney Pt	349-1970
Tripletail Seafood	4870 S Tamiami Trl	529-0555
Veronica Fish & Oyster	1830 S Osprey Ave	366-1342
Walt's Fish Market	4144 S Tamiami Trl	921-4605

STEAKHOUSE		
Alpine Steakhouse	4520 S Tamiami Trl	922-3797
Chaz 51 Steakhouse	549 US-41 BYP	484-6200
Connors Steakhouse	3501 S Tamiami Trl	260-3232
Rosebud's Steakhouse	2215 S Tamiami Trl	918-8771
The Summer House	149 Avenida Messina	206-2675

ANNA MARIA, BRADENTON, & PALMETTO

Restaurant Name	Address	Phone #
Atria Bread + Coffee	4120 LWR Blvd	751-1016
Beach Bistro	6600 Gulf Dr N	778-6444
Birdrock Taco Shack	1213 13th Ave W	545-9966
The Breakfast Company	7246 55th Ave E	201-6002
Double Deez Hot Dogs	3009 Gulf Dr N	251-5595
Graze Street AMI	3218 E Bay Dr	896-6320
Mean Deans Local Kitch	6059 26th St W	251-5435
Pier 22	1200 1st Avenue W	748-8087
Post Kitchen + Bar	8433 Cooper Ck Blvd	259-4850
Vacci Pizza & Cucina	4406 53rd Ave E	405-4131
Vernona	711 Manatee Ave E	284-0416

DOWNTOWN

Amore	180 N Lime Ave	383-1111
Azul Steak & Sushi	1296 First St	343-2122
Bar Hana	1289 N Palm Ave	536-9717
Beso	30 S Lemon Ave	279-2999
Bavaro's Pizza	27 Fletcher Ave	552-9131
Bevardi's Salute!	23 N Lemon Ave	365-1020
Bijou Cafe	1287 First St	366-8111
BLVD Cafe	1580 Blvd of the Arts	203-8102
Boca Sarasota	21 S Lemon Ave	256-3565
The Breakfast House	1817 Fruitville Rd	366-6860
Brick's Smoked Meats	1528 State St	993-1435
Café Epicure	1298 Main St	366-5648
Caragiulos	69 S Palm Ave	951-0866

DOWNTOWN		
Restaurant Name	Address	Phone #
C'est La Vie!	1553 Main St	906-9575
Circo	1435 2nd St	253-0978
Clasico Italian Chophse	1341 Main St	957-0700
Doggystyle	1544 Main St	260-5835
Drunken Poet Café	1572 Main St	955-8404
Duval's, Fresh, Local...	1435 Main St	312-4001
El Melvin Cocina	1355 Main St	366-1618
1592 Wood Fired Kitch	1592 Main St	365-2234
481 Gourmet	481 N Orange Ave	362-0400
Il Panificio	1703 Main St	366-5570
Indigenous	239 Links Ave	706-4740
Jack Dusty	1111 Ritz-Carlton Dr	309-2266
Kojo	1289 N Palm Ave	536-9717
Lila	1576 Main St	296-1042
Made	1990 Main St	953-2900
Main Bar Sandwich Shp	1944 Main St	955-8733
Mandeville Beer Garden	428 N Lemon Ave	954-8688
Marina Jack's	2 Marina Plaza	365-4243
Mattison's City Grille	1 N Lemon Ave	330-0440
Mediterraneo	1970 Main St	365-4122
Melange	1568 Main St	953-7111
Michelle's Brown Bag	1819 Main St	365-5858
Molly's Pub	1562 Main St	366-7711
99 Bottles Taproom	1445 2nd St	487-7874
Namo Izakaya	1439 Main St	362-3332
O'Leary's Tiki Bar	5 Bayfront Dr	953-7505
Owen's Fish Camp	516 Burns Ct	951-6936

DOWNTOWN		
Restaurant Name	**Address**	**Phone #**
Palm Avenue Deli	1297 N Palm Ave	263-3742
Pastry Art Bakery	1512 Main St	955-7545
Patrick's 1481	1481 Main St	955-1481
Pho Cali	1578 Main St	955-2683
The Rosemary	411 N Orange Ave	955-7600
Rosemary & Thyme	511 N Orange Ave	955-7600
Sage	1216 1st St	445-5660
Selva Grill	1345 Main St	362-4427
Siegfried's Restaurant	1869 Fruitville Rd	330-9330
Spice Station	1438 Blvd of the Arts	343-2894
State St Eating House	1533 State St	951-1533
Station 400	400 Lemon Ave	906-1400
Tamiami Tap	711 S Osprey Ave	500-3182
Toastique	10 S Lemon Ave	312-4099
Turmeric	1001 Cocoanut Ave	212-2622
Tzeva	1255 N Palm Ave	413-7425
Wolfie's Rascal House	1454 Blvd of the Arts	312-4072

GULF GATE		
Brine Seafood	2250 Gulf Gate Dr	404-5639
Dolce Italia	6606 Superior Ave	921-7007
Food + Beer	6528 Superior Ave	952-3361
Kiyoski's Sushi	6550 Gateway Ave	924-3781
Kolukan	6644 Gateway Ave	921-3133
Lovely Square	6559 Gateway Ave	724-2512
Monk's Steamer Bar	6690 Superior Ave	927-3388
Munchies 420 Café	6639 Superior Ave	929-9893

GULF GATE

Restaurant Name	Address	Phone #
Piccolo Italian Market	6518 Gateway Ave	923-2202
Schnitzel Kitchen	6521 Superior Ave	922-9299
Screaming Goat Taq.	6606 Superior Ave	210-3992
Tony's Chicago Beef	6569 Superior Ave	922-7979
Word of Mouth	6604 Gateway Ave	925-2400

LONGBOAT KEY & LIDO KEY

Drift Kitchen	700 Benjamin Franklin	388-2161
Dry Dock Waterfront	412 Gulf of Mexico Dr	383-0102
Euphemia Haye	5540 Gulf of Mexico Dr	383-3633
Lazy Lobster	5350 Gulf of Mexico Dr	388-0440
Lynches Pub & Grub	19 N Blvd of Pres	388-5550
Harry's Continental Kit.	525 St Judes Dr	383-0777
Maison Blanche	2605 Gulf of Mexico Dr	383-8088
Mar-Vista Restaurant	760 Broadway St	383-2391
New Pass Grill	1505 Ken Thompson	388-3050

LAKEWOOD RANCH & UNIVERSITY PARK

Apollonia Grill	8235 Cooper Creek	359-4816
Cassariano	8209 Natures Way	355-8615
Dim Sum King	8194 Tourist Center Dr	306-5848
GROVE Restaurant	10670 Boardwalk Lp	893-4321
Jpan Sushi & Grill	229 N Cattlemen Rd	954-5726
Jersey Girl Bagels	5275 University Pkwy	388-8910
Mademoiselle Paris	8527 Cooper Creek Bl	355-2323
Oak & Stone	5405 University Pkwy	225-4590
Tandoor	8453 Cooper Creek	926-3070

NORTH TAMIAMI TRAIL		
Restaurant Name	Address	Phone #
Fork & Hen	2801 N Tamiami Trl	960-1212
Hob Nob Drive-In	1701 Washington Blvd	955-5001
The Mable	2831 N Tamiami Trl	487-7373
Toasted Mango Café	430 N Tamiami Trl	388-7728
Wicked Cantina	1603 N Tamiami Trl	821-2990

ST. ARMANDS KEY		
Blu Kouzina	25 N Blvd of Pres	388-2619
Café L'Europe	431 St Armands Cir	388-4415
Cha Cha Coconuts	417 St Armands Cir	388-3300
The Columbia	411 St Armands Cir	388-3987
Crab & Fin	420 St Armands Cir	388-3964
Lobstercraft	28 S Blvd of Pres	346-6325
Madison Avenue Deli	28 N Blvd of Pres	388-3354
Shore Diner	465 John Ringling Blvd	296-0303
Speaks Clam Bar	29 N Blvd of Pres	232-7633
Venizia	373 St Armands Cir	388-1400
Vernona	40 S Blvd of Pres	254-5877

SIESTA KEY		
Anna's Deli	6535 Midnight Pass	348-4888
Bean Coffeehouse	5138 Ocean Blvd	260-6400
Big Water Fish Market	6641 Midnight Pass	554-8101
Bonjour French Cafe	5214 Ocean Blvd	346-0600
Café Gabbiano	5104 Ocean Blvd	349-1423

SIESTA KEY		
Restaurant Name	**Address**	**Phone #**
Capt. Curt's Oyster Bar	1200 Old Stickney Pt	349-3885
Clayton's Siesta Grille	1256 Old Stickney Pt	349-2800
The Cottage	153 Avenida Messina	312-9300
Daiquiri Deck Raw Bar	5250 Ocean Blvd	349-8697
Flavio's Siesta Key	5239 Ocean Blvd	349-0995
Gilligan's Island Bar	5253 Ocean Blvd	349-4759
The Hub Baha Grill	5148 Ocean Blvd	349-6800
Il Panificio	215 Avenida Madera	800-5570
Island House Tap & Grl.	5110 Ocean Blvd	312-9205
The Lobster Pot	5157 Ocean Blvd	349-2323
Miguel's	6631 Midnight Pass	349-4024
The Old Salty Dog	5023 Ocean Blvd	349-0158
Ophelia's on the Bay	9105 Midnight Pass	349-2212
Siesta Key Oyster Bar	5238 Ocean Blvd	346-5443
Shebeen Irish Pub	6641 Midnight Pass	952-3070
Spearfish Grille	1265 Old Stickney Pt	349-1970
Star Thai & Sushi	240 Avenida Madera	217-6758
The Summer House	149 Avenida Messina	206-2675
Sun Garden Café	210 Avenida Madera	346-7170
Toasted Mango Café	6621 Midnight Pass	552-6485
Turtle's	8875 Midnight Pass	346-2207
Village Café	5133 Ocean Blvd	349-2822
SOUTH TAMIAMI TRAIL		
Almazonica Cerveceria	4141 S Tamiami Trl	260-5964
Capo Pazzo	2053 Reynolds St	487-8677

SOUTH TAMIAMI TRAIL		
Restaurant Name	Address	Phone #
Gecko's Grill & Pub	4870 S Tamiami Trl	923-8896
Alpine Steakhouse	4520 S Tamiami Trl	922-3797
Connors Steakhouse	3501 S Tamiami Trl	260-3232
DaRuMa Japanese	4910 S. Tamiami Trl	552-9465
Demetrio's Pizzeria	4410 S Tamiami Trl	922-1585
Dutch Valley Rest.	6731 S Tamiami Trl	924-1770
Florence & Spice Boys	4990 S Tamiami Trl	405-3890
Gentile Cheesesteaks	7523 S Tamiami Trl	926-0441
The Grasshopper	7253 S Tamiami Trl	923-3688
Marcello's Ristorante	4155 S Tamiami Trl	921-6794
Mattison's Forty One	7275 S Tamiami Trl	921-3400
Michael's On East	1212 East Ave	366-0007
Napule Ristorante	7129 S Tamiami Trl	556-9639
Phillippi Creek Oyster	5363 S Tamiami Trl	925-4444
Roessler's	2033 Vamo Way	966-5688
Sardinia	5770 S Tamiami Trl	702-8582
Stiks	4413 S Tamiami Trl	923-2742
Tripletail Seafood	4870 S Tamiami Trl	529-0555
Walt's Fish Market	4144 S Tamiami Trl	921-4605
Yummy House	1737 S Tamiami Trl	351-1688

SOUTHSIDE VILLAGE		
A Sprig of Thyme	1962 Hillview St	330-8890
Figaro Bistro	1944 Hillview St	960-2109
Ka Papa Cuisine	1830 S Osprey Ave	600-8590
Knick's Tavern & Grill	1818 S Osprey Ave	955-7761
Libby's Brasserie	1917 S Osprey Ave	487-7300

SOUTHSIDE VILLAGE		
Restaurant Name	Address	Phone #
Meliora	1920 Hillview St	444-7692
Origin Beer & Pizza	3837 Hillview St	316-9222
Osteria Southside	1812 S Osprey Ave	361-3200
Pacific Rim	1859 Hillview St	330-8071
Veronica Fish & Oyster	1830 S Osprey Ave	366-1342

SOUTHGATE		
Andrea's	2085 Siesta Dr	951-9200
Baker & Wife	2157 Siesta Dr	960-1765
The Chateau Sarasota	2001 Siesta Dr	706-4093
Connors Steakhouse	3501 S Tamiami Trl	260-3232
Fleming's Steakhouse	2001 Siesta Dr	358-9463
Malmosto	2085 Siesta Dr	706-1460
Rick's French Bistro	2177 Siesta Dr	957-0533

UNIVERSITY TOWN CENTER (UTC)		
Brio Tuscan Grille	190 Univ Town Ctr Dr	702-9102
The Capital Grille	180 Univ Town Ctr Dr	256-3647
Cheesecake Factory	130 Univ Town Ctr Dr	256-3760
Kona Grill	150 Univ Town Ctr Dr	256-8005
Seasons 52	170 Univ Town Ctr Dr	702-9652
Sophies	120 Univ Town Ctr Dr	444-3077

We've Got Your Sarasota Restaurant News!

SUBSCRIBE TODAY

sarasota bites

LIVE MUSIC		
Restaurant Name	Address	Phone #
Birdrock Taco Shack	1213 13th Ave W	545-9966
Capt. Curt's Oyster Bar	1200 Old Stickney Pt	349-3885
Casey Key Fish House	801 Blackburn Pt Rd	966-1901
Gecko's Grill & Pub	4870 S Tamiami Trl	923-8896
Gilligan's Island Bar	5253 Ocean Blvd	349-4759
The Hub Baha Grill	5148 Ocean Blvd	349-6800
JR's Old Packinghouse	987 S Packinghouse	371-9358
Marina Jack's	2 Marina Plaza	365-4243
Mattison's City Grille	1 N Lemon Ave	330-0440
Mattison's Forty One	7275 S Tamiami Trl	921-3400
Nancy's Bar-B-Que	14475 SR 70	999-2390
O'Leary's Tiki Bar	5 Bayfront Dr	953-7505
Parrot Patio Bar & Grill	3602 Webber St	952-3352
Pop's Sunset Grill	112 Circuit Rd	488-3177
Sharky's on the Pier	1600 Harbor Dr S	488-1456
Siesta Key Oyster Bar	5238 Ocean Blvd	346-5443
Star Thai & Sushi	240 Avenida Madera	217-6758
Stottlemeyer's Smokehs	19 East Rd	312-5969
Tamiami Tap	711 S Osprey Ave	500-3182
Walt's Fish Market	4144 S Tamiami Trl	921-4605

CATERING		
Brick's Smoked Meats	1528 State St	993-1435
Daiquiri Deck Raw Bar	5250 Ocean Blvd	349-8697
Gecko's Grill & Pub	4870 S Tamiami Trl	923-8896
Harry's Continental Kit.	525 St Judes Dr	383-0777
JR's Old Packinghouse	987 S Packinghouse	371-9358

CATERING		
Restaurant Name	**Address**	**Phone #**
Mattison's Forty One	7275 S Tamiami Trl	921-3400
Michael's On East	1212 East Ave	366-0007
Nancy's Bar-B-Que	301 S Pineapple Ave	366-2271
Nellie's Deli	15 S Beneva Rd	924-2705
Village Café	5133 Ocean Blvd	349-2822
Zildjian Catering	6986 S Beneva Rd.	363-1709
EASY ON YOUR WALLET		
Athens Family Rest.	2300 Bee Ridge Rd	706-4121
Atria Bread + Coffee	4120 LWR Blvd	751-1016
Anna's Deli	6535 Midnight Pass	348-4888
Bean Coffeehouse	5138 Ocean Blvd	260-6400
The Breakfast House	1817 Fruitville Rd	366-6860
Casa Masa	2773 Bee Ridge Rd.	922-8226
Casey Key Fish House	801 Blackburn Pt Rd	966-1901
Circo	1435 2nd St	253-0978
Double Deez Hot Dogs	3009 Gulf Dr N	251-5595
Dim Sum King	8194 Tourist Center Dr	306-5848
Doggystyle	1544 Main St	260-5835
Dutch Valley Rest.	6731 S Tamiami Trl	924-1770
El Toro Bravo	2720 Stickney Pt	924-0006
Faicco's Italian Heros	3590 Webber St	960-1395
Gentile Cheesesteaks	7523 S Tamiami Trl	926-0441
Hob Nob Drive-In	1701 Washington Blvd	955-5001
Joey D's Chicago Style	3811 Kenny Dr.	378-8900

EASY ON YOUR WALLET		
Restaurant Name	**Address**	**Phone #**
Il Panificio	1703 Main St	366-5570
Island House Taqueria	2773 Bee Ridge Rd	922-8226
Jersey Girl Bagels	5275 University Pkwy	388-8910
Lovely Square	6559 Gateway Ave	724-2512
The Mable	2831 N Tamiami Trl	487-7373
Main Bar Sandwich Shp	1944 Main St	955-8733
Michelle's Brown Bag	1819 Main St	365-5858
Munchies 420 Café	6639 Superior Ave	929-9893
New Pass Grill	1505 Ken Thompson	388-3050
Pastry Art Bakery	1512 Main St	955-7545
Pho Cali	1578 Main St	955-2683
Piccolo Italian Market	6518 Gateway Ave	923-2202
Reyna's Taqueria	935 N Beneva Rd	260-8343
Screaming Goat Taq.	6606 Superior Ave	210-3992
Stiks	4413 S Tamiami Trl	923-2742
Tony's Chicago Beef	6569 Superior Ave	922-7979
Yoder's Restaurant	3434 Bahia Vista	955-7771
Yokoso Ramen	3422 Clark Rd	265-1600
Wicked Cantina	1603 N Tamiami Trl	821-2990

BREAKFAST & LUNCH		
Anna's Deli	6535 Midnight Pass	348-4888
Baby Brie's Cafe	1938 Adams Ln	362-0988
BLVD Cafe	1580 Blvd of the Arts	203-8102
Bonjour French Cafe	5214 Ocean Blvd	346-0600
The Breakfast Company	7246 55th Ave E	201-6002

BREAKFAST & LUNCH		
Restaurant Name	**Address**	**Phone #**
Atria Bread + Coffee	4120 LWR Blvd	751-1016
Bean Coffeehouse	5138 Ocean Blvd	260-6400
The Breakfast House	1817 Fruitville Rd	366-6860
Lovely Square	6559 Gateway Ave	724-2512
Main Bar Sandwich Shp	1944 Main St	955-8733
Michelle's Brown Bag	1819 Main St	365-5858
Millie's Cafe	3900 Clark Rd	923-4054
Oasis Cafe	3542 S Osprey Ave	957-1214
Pastry Art Bakery	1512 Main St	955-7545
The Rosemary	411 N Orange Ave	955-7600
Station 400	400 Lemon Ave	906-1400
Sun Garden Café	210 Avenida Madera	346-7170
Toasted Mango Café	6621 Midnight Pass	552-6485
Toastique	10 S Lemon Ave	312-4099
Village Café	5133 Ocean Blvd	349-2822
Word of Mouth	6604 Gateway Ave	925-2400
NEW		
Azul Steak & Sushi	1296 First St	343-2122
Bar Hana	1289 N Palm Ave	536-9717
Bay Leaf Indian Cuisine	1092 S Tamiami	244-0310
Beso	30 S Lemon Ave	279-2999
Capo Pazzo	2053 Reynolds St	487-8677
The Chateau Sarasota	2001 Siesta Dr	706-4093
Chaz 51 Steakhouse	549 US-41 BYP	484-6200
Deep Lagoon Seafood	482 Blackburn Pt Rd	770-3337
Double Deez Hot Dogs	3009 Gulf Dr N	251-5595

NEW		
Restaurant Name	Address	Phone #
Fat Point Brewing	257 N Cattlemen Rd	491-2827
F.L.A. Deli	2805 Proctor Rd	217-5710
Florence & Spice Boys	4990 S Tamiami Trl	405-3890
Kolukan	6644 Gateway Ave	921-3133
The Mable	2831 N Tamiami Trl	487-7373
Malmosto	2085 Siesta Dr	706-1460
Meshugana Deli	4001 Clark Rd	933-0244
Namo Izakaya	1439 Main St	362-3332
Osteria 500	1580 Lakefront Dr	866-8962
Osteria Southside	1812 S Osprey Ave	361-3200
Palm Avenue Deli	1297 N Palm Ave	263-3742
Pigfish	5377 McIntosh Rd	777-5220
Post Kitchen + Bar	8433 Cooper Ck Blvd	259-4850
Shebeen Irish Pub	6641 Midnight Pass	952-3070
So French Cafe	6280 Lockwood Rdg	388-8936
Tzeva	1255 N Palm Ave	413-7425
Vacci Pizza & Cucina	4406 53rd Ave E	405-4131
Vernona	711 Manatee Ave E	284-0416
Wolfie's Rascal House	1454 Blvd of the Arts	312-4072

SUSHI		
Azul Steak & Sushi	1296 First St	343-2122
Blue Koi	3801 Macintosh Rd	388-7738
DaRuMa Japanese	5459 Fruitville Rd	342-6600
DaRuMa Japanese	4910 S. Tamiami Trl	552-9465
Drunken Poet Café	1572 Main St	955-8404
Jpan Sushi & Grill	3800 S Tamiami Trl	954-5726

SUSHI		
Restaurant Name	**Address**	**Phone #**
Jpan Sushi & Grill	229 N Cattlemen Rd	954-5726
Kiyoski's Sushi	6550 Gateway Ave	924-3781
Kojo	1289 N Palm Ave	536-9717
Pacific Rim	1859 Hillview St	330-8071
Spice Station	1438 Blvd of the Arts	343-2894
Star Thai & Sushi	240 Avenida Madera	217-6758

SPORTS + FOOD + FUN		
Capt. Curt's Oyster Bar	1200 Old Stickney Pt	349-3885
Daiquiri Deck Raw Bar	5250 Ocean Blvd	349-8697
Gecko's Grill & Pub	6606 S Tamiami Trl	248-2020
Gecko's Grill & Pub	1900 Hillview St	953-2929
Gecko's Grill & Pub	5588 Palmer Crossing	923-6061
Oak & Stone	5405 University Pkwy	225-4590
The Old Salty Dog	5023 Ocean Blvd	349-0158
Parrot Patio Bar & Grill	3602 Webber St	952-3352
Patrick's 1481	1481 Main St	955-1481
Siesta Key Oyster Bar	5238 Ocean Blvd	346-5443

GREAT BURGERS		
Alpine Steakhouse	4520 S Tamiami Trl	922-3797
BrewBurgers Pub	360 Commercial Ct	484-2337
Cha Cha Coconuts	417 St Armands Cir	388-3300
Connors Steakhouse	3501 S. Tamiami Trl	260-3232
Gecko's Grill & Pub	4870 S Tamiami Trl	923-8896
Gecko's Grill & Pub	1900 Hillview St	953-2929

GREAT BURGERS

Restaurant Name	Address	Phone #
Gecko's Grill & Pub	5588 Palmer Crossing	923-6061
Gecko's Grill & Pub	351 N Cattlemen Rd	378-0077
Food + Beer	6528 Superior Ave	952-3361
Hob Nob Drive-In	1701 Washington Blvd	955-5001
Indigenous	239 Links Ave	706-4740
Island House Tap & Grl.	5110 Ocean Blvd	312-9205
JR's Old Packinghouse	987 S Packinghouse	371-9358
Knick's Tavern & Grill	1818 S Osprey Ave	955-7761
Libby's Brasserie	1917 S Osprey Ave	487-7300
The Mable	2831 N Tamiami Trl	487-7373
Made	1990 Main St	953-2900
Munchies 420 Café	6639 Superior Ave	929-9893
New Pass Grill	1505 Ken Thompson	388-3050
Parrot Patio Bar & Grill	3602 Webber St	952-3352
Patrick's 1481	1481 Main St	955-1481
Pop's Sunset Grill	112 Circuit Rd	488-3177
Shakespeare's	3550 S Osprey Ave	364-5938
Sharky's on the Pier	1600 Harbor Dr S	488-1456
Tony's Chicago Beef	6569 Superior Ave	922-7979

NICE WINE LIST

Amore	180 N Lime Ave	383-1111
Andrea's	2085 Siesta Dr	951-9200
Baker & Wife	2157 Siesta Dr	960-1765
Beach Bistro	6600 Gulf Dr N	778-6444

NICE WINE LIST		
Restaurant Name	**Address**	**Phone #**
Bevardi's Salute!	23 N Lemon Ave	365-1020
Bijou Café	1287 First St	366-8111
Café Barbosso	5501 Palmer Crossing	922-7999
Café Gabbiano	5104 Ocean Blvd	349-1423
Café L'Europe	431 St Armands Cir	388-4415
Cassariano	313 W Venice Ave	786-1000
The Chateau Sarasota	2001 Siesta Dr	706-4093
Chaz 51 Steakhouse	549 US-41 BYP	484-6200
Connors Steakhouse	3501 S Tamiami Trl	260-3232
Dolce Italia	6606 Superior Ave	921-7007
Duval's, Fresh, Local...	1435 Main St	312-4001
Euphemia Haye	5540 Gulf of Mexico Dr	383-3633
Figaro Bistro	1944 Hillview St	960-2109
Fins At Sharky's	1600 Harbor Dr S	999-3467
Flavio's Siesta Key	5239 Ocean Blvd	349-0995
GROVE Restaurant	10670 Boardwalk Lp	893-4321
Harry's Continental Kit.	525 St Judes Dr	383-0777
Indigenous	239 Links Ave	706-4740
Jack Dusty	1111 Ritz-Carlton Dr	309-2266
Maison Blanche	2605 Gulf of Mexico Dr	383-8088
Mattison's Forty One	7275 S Tamiami Trl	921-3400
Melange	1568 Main St	953-7111
Michael's On East	1212 East Ave	366-0007
Miguel's	6631 Midnight Pass	349-4024
Napule Ristorante	7129 S Tamiami Trl	556-9639
Ophelia's on the Bay	9105 Midnight Pass	349-2212

NICE WINE LIST		
Restaurant Name	Address	Phone #
Pier 22	1200 1st Avenue W	748-8087
Roessler's	2033 Vamo Way	966-5688
Rosebud's Steakhouse	2215 S Tamiami Trl	918-8771
Rosemary & Thyme	511 N Orange Ave	955-7600
Sage	1216 1st St	445-5660
Sardinia	5770 S Tamiami Trl	702-8582
State St Eating House	1533 State St	951-1533
The Summer House	149 Avenida Messina	206-2675
Selva Grill	1345 Main St	362-4427
Tzeva	1255 N Palm Ave	413-7425
Veronica Fish & Oyster	1830 S Osprey Ave	366-1342

HELP MAKE A DIFFERENCE IN OUR SARASOTA-MANATEE COMMUNITY

Listed below are two local organizations that are striving to assist those in need in our Sarasota area. They could use your help. Please consider a donation to either (or both) during 2024.

ALL FAITHS FOOD BANK
WHAT THEY NEED: Donations of non-perishable, frozen, and perishable food items needed. Monetary donations are also accepted and can be made directly through their website.
MORE INFO: allfaithsfoodbank.org

MAYOR'S FEED THE HUNGRY PROGRAM
WHAT THEY NEED: Donations of food, time, and money are needed. This program hosts a large food drive in the month of November. Check their website for details or to make a monetary donation.
MORE INFO: mayorsfeedthehungry.org

A BEAUTIFUL WATER VIEW		
Restaurant Name	**Address**	**Phone #**
Beach Bistro	6600 Gulf Dr N	778-6444
Casey Key Fish House	801 Blackburn Pt Rd	966-1901
The Crow's Nest	1968 Tarpon Ctr Dr	484-9551
Deep Lagoon Seafood	482 Blackburn Pt Rd	770-3337
Drift Kitchen	700 Benjamin Franklin	388-2161
Dry Dock Waterfront	412 Gulf of Mexico Dr	383-0102
Fins At Sharky's	1600 Harbor Dr S	999-3467
Jack Dusty	1111 Ritz-Carlton Dr	309-2266
Mar-Vista Restaurant	760 Broadway St	383-2391
Marina Jack's	2 Marina Plaza	365-4243
New Pass Grill	1505 Ken Thompson	388-3050
The Old Salty Dog	160 Ken Thompson Pk	388-4311
The Old Salty Dog	1485 S Tamiami Trl	483-1000
O'Leary's Tiki Bar	5 Bayfront Dr	953-7505
Ophelia's on the Bay	9105 Midnight Pass	349-2212
Phillippi Creek Oyster	5363 S Tamiami Trl	925-4444
Pier 22	1200 1st Avenue W	748-8087
Pop's Sunset Grill	112 Circuit Rd	488-3177
Sharky's on the Pier	1600 Harbor Dr S	488-1456
Turtle's	8875 Midnight Pass	346-2207

LATER NIGHT MENU		
Azul Steak & Sushi	1296 First St	343-2122
Bar Hana	1289 N Palm Ave	536-9717
Café Epicure	1298 Main St	366-5648
Capt. Curt's Oyster Bar	1200 Old Stickney Pt	349-3885
Casey Key Fish House	801 Blackburn Pt Rd	966-1901

LATER NIGHT MENU		
Restaurant Name	Address	Phone #
Circo	1435 2nd St	253-0978
The Cottage	153 Avenida Messina	312-9300
Daiquiri Deck Raw Bar	5250 Ocean Blvd	349-8697
Drunken Poet Café	1572 Main St	955-8404
El Melvin Cocina	1355 Main St	366-1618
Flavio's Siesta Key	5239 Ocean Blvd	349-0995
Food + Beer	6528 Superior Ave	952-3361
Gecko's Grill & Pub	6606 S Tamiami Trl	248-2020
Gecko's Grill & Pub	1900 Hillview St	953-2929
Gilligan's Island Bar	5253 Ocean Blvd	349-4759
The Hub Baha Grill	5148 Ocean Blvd	349-6800
Island House Tap & Grl.	5110 Ocean Blvd	312-9205
JR's Old Packinghouse	987 S Packinghouse	371-9358
The Mable	2831 N Tamiami Trl	487-7373
Made	1990 Main St	953-2900
Mattison's City Grille	1 N Lemon Ave	330-0440
Melange	1568 Main St	953-7111
Monk's Steamer Bar	6690 Superior Ave	927-3388
Munchies 420 Café	6639 Superior Ave	929-9893
Origin Beer & Pizza	3837 Hillview St	316-9222
Palm Avenue Deli	1297 N Palm Ave	263-3742
Patrick's 1481	1481 Main St	955-1481
Sharky's on the Pier	1600 Harbor Dr S	488-1456
Siesta Key Oyster Bar	5238 Ocean Blvd	346-5443
Tamiami Tap	711 S Osprey Ave	500-3182
Walt's Fish Market	4144 S Tamiami Trl	921-4605
Wolfie's Rascal House	1454 Blvd of the Arts	312-4072

SARASOTA FINE & FINER DINING		
Restaurant Name	Address	Phone #
A Sprig of Thyme	1962 Hillview St	330-8890
Andrea's	2085 Siesta Dr	951-9200
Beach Bistro	6600 Gulf Dr N	778-6444
Bijou Café	1287 First St	366-8111
Café L'Europe	431 St Armands Cir	388-4415
The Crow's Nest	1968 Tarpon Ctr Dr	484-9551
Euphemia Haye	5540 Gulf of Mexico Dr	383-3633
Indigenous	239 Links Ave	706-4740
Jack Dusty	1111 Ritz-Carlton Dr	309-2266
Maison Blanche	2605 Gulf of Mexico Dr	383-8088
Melange	1568 Main St	953-7111
Michael's On East	1212 East Ave	366-0007
Ophelia's on the Bay	9105 Midnight Pass	349-2212
Pier 22	1200 1st Avenue W	748-8087
Sage	1216 1st St	445-5660
The Summer House	149 Avenida Messina	206-2675
PIZZA PIE!		
Baker & Wife	2157 Siesta Dr	960-1765
Bavaro's Pizza	27 Fletcher Ave	552-9131
Café Barbosso	5501 Palmer Crossing	922-7999
Café Epicure	1298 Main St	366-5648
Capo Pazzo	2053 Reynolds St	487-8677
Caragiulos	69 S Palm Ave	951-0866
1592 Wood Fired Kitch	1592 Main St	365-2234
Flavio's Siesta Key	5239 Ocean Blvd	349-0995

PIZZA PIE!		
Restaurant Name	Address	Phone #
Il Panificio	1703 Main St	366-5570
Joey D's Chicago Style	3811 Kenny Dr.	378-8900
Malmosto	2085 Siesta Dr	706-1460
Mattison's City Grille	1 N Lemon Ave	330-0440
Mediterraneo	1970 Main St	365-4122
Napule Ristorante	7129 S Tamiami Trl	556-9639
Oak & Stone	5405 University Pkwy	225-4590
Origin Beer & Pizza	3837 Hillview St	316-9222
Vacci Pizza & Cucina	4406 53rd Ave E	405-4131
Venizia	373 St Armands Cir	388-1400

UPSCALE CHAIN DINING		
Bonefish Grill	3971 S Tamiami Trl	924-9090
Bravo Coastal Kitchen	3501 S Tamiami Trl	316-0868
Brio Tuscan Grille	190 Univ Town Ctr Dr	702-9102
The Chart House	201 Gulf of Mex Dr	383-5593
California Pizza Kitchen	192 N Cattlemen Rd	203-6966
The Capital Grille	180 Univ Town Ctr Dr	256-3647
Cooper's Hawk	3130 Fruitville Comm	263-8100
Fleming's Steakhouse	2001 Siesta Dr	358-9463
Hyde Park Steakhouse	35 S Lemon Ave	366-7788
Kona Grill	150 Univ Town Ctr Dr	256-8005
P.F. Chang's	766 S Osprey Ave	296-6002
Ruth's Chris Steakhouse	6700 S Tamiaml Trl	924-9442
Seasons 52	170 Univ Town Ctr Dr	702-9652
Tommy Bahama Rest	300 John Ringling Blv	388-2888

Printed in the USA
CPSIA information can be obtained
at www.ICGtesting.com
LVHW080604290124
769933LV00013B/391